WeightWatchers®

Everyday Favourites

First published in Great Britain by Simon & Schuster UK Ltd, 2013
A CBS COMPANY

13 5 7 9 10 8 6 4 2

Simon & Schuster UK Ltd, 1st Floor, 222 Gray's Inn Road, London WC1X 8HB
www.simonandschuster.co.uk
Simon & Schuster Australia, Sydney
Simon & Schuster India, New Delhi

A CIP catalogue copy for this book is available from the British Library.

Weight Watchers Publications Team: Jane Griffiths, Nina McKerlie and Donna Watts

Simon & Schuster Project Management: WordWorks
Photography: Steve Baxter *Prop styling:* Jenny Iggledon
Food styling: Sue Ashworth
Hand model: Anna Hitchin
Design and typesetting: Lisa Tai
Colour reproduction by Dot Gradations Ltd, UK
Printed in Italy

Picture credit: Fresh Fruit in a Bowl, page 8, © Robert Kneschke @ www.shutterstock.com
Bowl and Spoon with Yogurt, page 11, © www.colourbox.com

Pictured on the front cover: Beef, Ale and Mushroom Pie, page 184

Pictured on the back cover: Veg Mac 'n' Cheese, page 88; Prawn Cocktail Pitta, page 30;
Weekday Roast Red Pepper Chicken with Baby Roasties, page 108; Strawberry Posset, page 200

WeightWatchers®
Everyday Favourites

Satisfying meal choices the family will love, for every day of the week

Nicola Graimes

**SIMON &
SCHUSTER
ILLUSTRATED**

London · New York · Sydney · Toronto · New Delhi

A CBS COMPANY

ProPoints® value logo: You'll find this easy to read **ProPoints** value logo on every recipe throughout this book. The logo represents the number of **ProPoints** values per serving each recipe contains. It is not an indication of the fillingness of a recipe.

Weight Watchers **ProPoints** Weight Loss System is a simple way to lose weight. As part of the Weight Watchers **ProPoints** plan you'll enjoy eating delicious, healthy, filling foods that help to keep you feeling satisfied for longer and in control of your portions.

Filling & Healthy foods are highlighted in green. Focus on these foods where you can – they are healthy choices that will help you to feel satisfied for longer.

V This symbol denotes a vegetarian recipe and assumes that, where relevant, free range eggs, vegetarian cheese, vegetarian virtually fat-free fromage frais, vegetarian low fat crème fraîche and vegetarian low fat yogurts are used. Virtually fat-free fromage frais, low fat crème fraîche and low fat yogurts may contain traces of gelatine so they are not always vegetarian. Please check the labels.

❄ This symbol denotes a dish that can be frozen. Unless otherwise stated, you can freeze the finished dish for up to 1 month. Defrost thoroughly and reheat until the dish is piping hot throughout.

RECIPE NOTES

Egg size: Medium unless otherwise stated.

Raw eggs: Only the freshest eggs should be used. Pregnant women, the elderly and children should avoid recipes with eggs which are not fully cooked or raw.

All fruits and vegetables: Medium unless otherwise stated.

Chocolate: Use chocolate with a minimum of 70% cocoa solids.

Low fat spread: Where a recipe states to use a low fat spread, a light spread with a fat content of no less than 38% should be used.

Stock: Stock cubes should be used in the recipes, unless otherwise stated. Prepare them according to the packet instructions, unless directed otherwise.

Microwaves: Microwave timings are for an 850 watt microwave oven.

Recipe timings: These are approximate and meant to be guidelines. Please note that the preparation time includes all the steps up to and following the main cooking time(s), including making any other recipes.

Low fat soft cheese: Where a recipe states to use low fat soft cheese, a soft cheese with a fat content of less than 5% should be used.

Contents

THE GROUND-BREAKING *PROPOINTS*® PLAN

OUR OVERLOADED FOOD ENVIRONMENT

We live in a **challenging world** of unparalleled exposure to high-fat, high-calorie, heavily promoted, inexpensive and widely available food. Add our modern sedentary lifestyles to the mix and it's no surprise we're facing a growing obesity epidemic.

Now new brain-scanning technology is proving that this modern environment has a huge impact on our eating behaviour. The urge to eat is driven from deep within the brain and is triggered by the influence of **highly palatable food, which is all around us**.

TAKE BACK CONTROL
Food is a great pleasure in life and enjoying good food isn't something you should need to compromise on.

The great news is that you don't have to. The ground-breaking *ProPoints* plan will help you to reclaim control from today's food environment, showing you how to **shift your surroundings to work with you, not against you**.

Do this in **small, achievable steps**, and with practice, it will become routine – and easy.

It's Not All About Willpower

Do you ever find yourself 'suddenly having room' for dessert when it's offered to you only moments after a rich and filling meal, when you thought you couldn't possibly eat another bite? Well, don't blame yourself – breakthrough scientific research* is showing it's not a lack of willpower that's driving us to eat more and gain more, but the overloaded food environment itself. Scientists have discovered that the brain is hard-wired to trigger an urge to eat in response to the sights, smells, even the thoughts of our favourite high-calorie foods, whether they're chips or cheese, biscuits or burgers. The *ProPoints* plan will help you find practical, realistic and simple solutions for creating an environment that actively supports your weight loss rather than works against it.

RECLAIM CONTROL //
Stop feeling guilty
Start taking charge

To find our more about the impact of the overloaded food environment on your weight, **scan me or go to weightwatchers.co.uk/foodenvironment
** Available to subscribers only

---

* Carnell S et al. Neuroimaging and obesity: current knowledge and future directions. Obes Rev. 2012 Jan; 13(1): 43-56.

RECLAIM CONTROL OF YOUR KITCHEN

Your kitchen is just one environment that you can, to a certain extent at least, reclaim control over. Just seeing tempting food can trigger cravings so start your journey by **re-organising your kitchen** – turning it into a **weight loss haven** that supports your weight loss.

Successful weight loss for the long haul is a step-by-step journey and not a quick fix. But **small changes** eventually add up to a big change. By starting to make small changes and developing new manageable routines, you'll still be able to live in the 'real world' whilst losing weight, and once the weight is off, you'll have developed some healthy routines that will help you to keep the weight off for good.

To get you started, here are some ideas for small, easy steps that you can take to help you on your weight loss journey:

- Put your 'trigger' foods in opaque containers and **stash them out of sight** (the family can still get to them, but you don't have to have them in view).
- Have lovely vegetables and **low *ProPoints* value options within easy reach**.
- **Plan your meals for the week** and write a shopping list, so that you remain in control whilst out food shopping.
- Have some **zero *ProPoints* value vegetable crudités in the fridge**, ready for you to nibble on when you come in from work peckish.

COOK THE WEIGHT WATCHERS WAY

Armed with this cookbook you'll discover how easy it is to create delicious, healthy food to enjoy with your family every single day. Not only do you get 120 recipes **specially written for the *ProPoints* plan**, you'll also learn about healthy cooking methods, essential low-fat store cupboard ingredients and instant swaps that make pulling a healthy meal together so much easier. Cooking the Weight Watchers way will soon become effortless – a matter of routine – and your kitchen will support your weight loss every step of the way.

RECLAIM CONTROL //

Cooking the Weight Watchers
way will support your weight
loss every step of the way.

Healthy Snacks

When you get home from work, do you go straight to the kitchen and start looking for a snack right away? In between meals, do you find yourself prowling around the kitchen for something tasty? We all do. *Reach for some healthy nibbles and take back control.*

Stacking your kitchen with appealing, low **ProPoints** value foods like those below means you can satisfy your snacking urges without taking a big chunk out of your **ProPoints** budget…

SAVOURY SNACKS

	ProPoints value per serving
• 60 g crumpet	2
• 6 slices Melba toast	2
• Weight Watchers Bagel, toasted	4
• 1 x 55 g teacake	5
• 2 Jacobs Cream Crackers	2
+ 2 teaspoons low fat spread	1
• Vegetable crudités (carrots, peppers, cucumber)	0

TASTY TOPPINGS

• Weight Watchers Low Fat Cheese Triangle	1
• 1 mini Babybel Light	1
• 1 tbsp (30 g) reduced fat houmous	2
• 150 g portion reduced fat cottage cheese	3
• 15 g smooth or crunchy peanut butter	3
• 2 teaspoons low fat spread	1

ON THE SIDE

	ProPoints value per serving
• Virtually fat free plain yogurt, 150 g pot, with banana or grapes	2
• 150 g pot 0% fat Greek yogurt	2

NIBBLES

• 25 g air popped popcorn	3
• 30 g Bombay mix	4
• 18 g pack Weight Watchers Cheese Puffs	2
• 24 g bag Walkers Lights	3

FRUIT AND SWEETS

• Fruit, fruit and more fruit	0
• 25 g dried banana chips	4
• Weight Watchers Pear & Peach Pots	0
• 12 g meringue nest	1
• Weight Watchers Carrot Cake Slice	2

FILLING & HEALTHY HELP

FILLING & HEALTHY FOODS

The **ProPoints** plan guides you to the most satisfying choices – foods that keep you feeling satisfied for longer and can actively help to reduce that overwhelming urge to eat. Called Filling & Healthy foods, they are the very best food choices for satisfaction, health and low **ProPoints** values. Because they're lower in energy density, you get fewer calories for more bulk, and they're lower in salt and fat but higher in fibre than other similar foods in their group.

You can find Filling & Healthy foods at a glance in this cookbook as they're highlighted in green, **like this**. Many of the recipes in this cookbook contain Filling & Healthy foods, which will help to keep you feeling fuller for longer.

To find out more about
Filling & Healthy foods,
**scan me or go to
weightwatchers.co.uk/
fillingandhealthy
**Available to subscribers only

TOP 20
Filling & Healthy foods

These are the 20 most common Filling & Healthy foods tracked by Weight Watchers Members (excluding fruit & vegetables).

SEE WHAT OTHER MEMBERS ARE ENJOYING TO STAY FULLER FOR LONGER.

★ Skimmed milk
★ Skinless chicken breast
★ Eggs
★ Porridge oats
★ Crumpets
★ Calorie controlled bread
★ Tuna in brine
★ Premium ham
★ Wafer thin ham
★ Baked beans

★ Pre-packed ham
★ Brown rice
★ Tuna in spring water
★ Extra lean beef mince
★ Salmon
★ Prawns
★ Bacon medallions
★ Wholemeal pasta
★ Unsweetened soya milk
★ 0% fat Greek yogurt

Be Empowered
You can find Filling & Healthy foods at a glance in this cookbook as they're highlighted in green, like this.

SMART CHOICES

MORE TO SPEND?

Think of this cookbook as a guide, giving you an all round basic knowledge of healthy cooking and eating. Experiment and explore and **make the recipes your own**. If you want to bulk up a recipe, adding a few extras – for yourself or other family members who don't need to lose weight – go ahead.

Throughout this cookbook, you'll find ideas for how to spend extra *ProPoints* values or fill up a hungry family even more.

A quick guide to extras

BULK IT OUT

Do curry a favour: 25 g cooked rice (**brown rice** is Filling & Healthy) adds **1 *ProPoints*** value

Comforting potatoes: 225 g (raw weight) **potato** baked in its skin is **5 *ProPoints*** values

Tasty and filling: 150 g portion of new **potatoes** is **3 *ProPoints*** values

Pasta please: 150 g portion of cooked **wholemeal pasta** is Filling & Healthy and **5 *ProPoints*** values

Make a meal special: 150 g roasted potatoes for **6 *ProPoints*** values

Fill up fast: 100 g of thick cut oven baked chips for **4 *ProPoints*** values

Super sausages: two grilled Weight Watchers Premium Pork Sausages for **3 *ProPoints*** values

ADD SOME MORE

Great with soups: a 60 g bread roll is **4 *ProPoints*** values

A favourite on the side: 105 g baked beans for **2 *ProPoints*** values

Wonderful with lamb: 1 tablespoon tzatziki for **1 *ProPoints*** value

Perfect with dessert: a 60 g scoop of low fat ice cream for **2 *ProPoints*** values

SWAP AND SAVE

Small changes can add up to a big difference. Once you begin swapping ingredients, you'll start saving a lot. For example, if you swap whole milk for skimmed, you'll save 2 **ProPoints** values for every ¼ pint. That could add up to a whopping 14 **ProPoints** values over just one week.

Making just one small change like this, every week, will soon make a big difference to your weight, and it's **a change that you can sustain for life**.

Small swaps for BIG savings

SWAP from	To this	ProPoints values SAVED
DAIRY		
medium fat soft cheese	low fat soft cheese (extra light)	**1 ProPoints** value for every 50 g portion
regular Cheddar cheese	half fat Cheddar	**2 ProPoints** values for every 40 g portion
1 large egg	1 medium egg	**1 ProPoints** value
Greek plain yogurt	0% fat Greek yogurt	**3 ProPoints** values for every 150 g pot
MEAT		
beef mince (raw)	extra lean beef mince (raw)	**3 ProPoints** values for every 125 g portion
lean beef mince (raw)	Quorn mince	**3 ProPoints** values for every 125 g portion
chicken breast with skin	skinless chicken breast	**2 ProPoints** values for every 165 g portion
OTHER		
regular mayonnaise	reduced fat mayonnaise	**2 ProPoints** values per tablespoon
a 60 g medium slice of sliced white or brown bread	2 slices (40 g) of calorie controlled bread	**1 ProPoints** value

On the go lunches

Beat the High Street environment with these delicious lunches to enjoy at home or take to work. Bring a packed lunch to work and you'll soon find you have a healthy eating routine.

Monday lunch soup

This hearty soup makes the most of any leftover meat from the Sunday roast – hence its name. This version uses lamb but you could try other types of roasted meat too. The soup can be thrown together on Sunday, divided into portions and reheated when you want it.

Serves 4

Preparation time 20 minutes

Cooking time 25 minutes

4 *ProPoints* values per serving

18 *ProPoints* values per recipe

calorie controlled cooking spray

1 large **onion**, chopped

2 **carrots**, peeled and sliced

175 g (6 oz) **swede**, peeled and diced

1.2 litres (2 pints) chicken stock

2 heaped tablespoons Thai red curry paste

2.5 cm (1 inch) **fresh root ginger**, peeled and sliced thinly

4 large handfuls of baby **spinach**

175 g (6 oz) cooked lean roast lamb, cut into bite size pieces

salt and freshly ground black pepper

1 Heat a large lidded saucepan, spray with the cooking spray and sauté the vegetables for 5 minutes.

2 Add the stock, curry paste and ginger, stir briefly and bring to the boil. Reduce the heat, part-cover the pan and cook for 25 minutes, or until the vegetables are tender. Add the spinach, cook for another 2 minutes and season.

3 Remove the soup from the heat and leave to cool. Just before serving, add the lamb and reheat for 5 minutes.

 Veggie swap

Instead of the lamb, add a 400 g can of **chick peas in water**, drained, for the same *ProPoints* values per person. Add to the soup with the spinach in Step 2 and use vegetable stock instead of the chicken stock.

 Make ahead

The soup can be made in advance. Prepare it up to the point where the lamb is added in Step 3, then leave to cool and transfer to a freezerproof lidded container. It will keep for up to 1 month, frozen.

Hungry family hint

A 50 g (1¾ oz) crusty roll or a medium size pitta bread will add 4 *ProPoints* values per serving.

Creamy sweetcorn soup

This chunky sweetcorn soup makes a perfect warming lunch, served with a 50 g (1¾ oz) wholemeal roll per person for an extra 3 *ProPoints* values per serving.

Serves 2

30 minutes in total

6 *ProPoints* values per serving

12 *ProPoints* values per recipe

1 large **leek**, sliced thinly

1 **carrot**, peeled and sliced thinly

1 **celery** stick, sliced thinly

calorie controlled cooking spray

175 g (6 oz) **potatoes**, peeled and diced

600 ml (20 fl oz) vegetable stock

2 bay leaves

326 g can **sweetcorn in water**, drained

100 ml (3½ fl oz) **skimmed milk**

1 tablespoon snipped **fresh chives** (optional)

salt and freshly ground black pepper

1 Put the leek, carrot and celery in a medium lidded saucepan, spray with the cooking spray and sauté for 5 minutes, stirring occasionally, until softened.

2 Add the potatoes, stock and bay leaves. Bring to the boil, then turn the heat down and simmer, part-covered, for 10 minutes, stirring the soup occasionally.

3 Add the sweetcorn and milk and cook for another 5 minutes until the vegetables and potato are tender. Season and stir in the chives, if using. Decant half the soup into a flask. Alternatively, transfer to a lidded container for reheating before eating. Allow the remaining soup to cool before storing, covered, in the fridge for up to 3 days, or freeze for up to 1 month.

Cajun turkey bagel

This filling bagel is just the thing to keep energy levels up throughout the afternoon. You could also swap the Cajun or fajita spice mix for your favourite blend of spices, or why not try curry powder?

Serves 1

15 minutes in total

8 *ProPoints* values per serving

8 *ProPoints* values per recipe

125 g (4½ oz) **lean turkey steak**

calorie controlled cooking spray

1 teaspoon Cajun or fajita spice mix

1 **Weight Watchers bagel**

1 teaspoon extra light mayonnaise

2 soft **lettuce leaves**

1 tablespoon chilled tomato salsa

salt and freshly ground black pepper

1 Spray both sides of the turkey steak with the cooking spray, then sprinkle with the spice mix and season.

2 Heat a griddle or non stick frying pan over a high heat and put the turkey in the pan. Reduce the heat to medium high and griddle for 6 minutes, turning once, until the turkey is golden on the outside with no trace of pink in the centre. Leave to cool.

3 Split the bagel in half, spread one half with the mayonnaise and top with the lettuce leaves. Put the turkey on top with the salsa and the second half of the bagel. Wrap in cling film and chill until ready to eat.

Make ahead

The turkey can be cooked and left to cool the night before. Wrap it in cling film and keep it in the fridge overnight before making the bagel.

More to spend?

If you have a few extra ***ProPoints*** values to spare, try a Weight Watchers Strawberry and Vanilla Flavour Mousse for dessert, for an extra 2 ***ProPoints*** values per serving.

Super
quick

Super
quick

Pâté, cucumber and mustard bagel

This filled bagel couldn't be more simple to make.

Serves 1
5 minutes in total
5 ProPoints values per serving
5 ProPoints values per recipe

15 g (½ oz) reduced fat smooth pâté
1 **Weight Watchers bagel**, split in half
2 soft **lettuce leaves**
6 slices **cucumber**
½ teaspoon wholegrain mustard

1 Spread the pâté over one half of the bagel and top with the lettuce and cucumber. Spread the mustard over the second half of the bagel and place on top of the filling.
2 Wrap the bagel in cling film and store it in the fridge. Allow the bagel to come to room temperature before eating.

More to spend?

If you have some **ProPoints** values to spare, team this delicious bagel with some crisps, such as a packet of Weight Watchers Ready Salted Crinkle Crisps, for an extra 2 **ProPoints** values per serving.

Beef salad naan pocket

Naan bread is perfect for filling and makes a refreshing option to everyday sliced bread.

Serves 1
10 minutes in total
6 ProPoints values per serving
6 ProPoints values per recipe

1 teaspoon extra light mayonnaise
1 teaspoon mango chutney
50 g (1¾ oz) cooked **lean roast beef**, sliced into thin strips
1 small **carrot**, peeled and grated
2.5 cm (1 inch) **cucumber**, sliced finely
1 **spring onion**, sliced
2 **lettuce leaves**, shredded
1 Weight Watchers naan bread
salt and freshly ground black pepper

1 Mix together the mayonnaise, mango chutney, beef, carrot, cucumber, spring onion and lettuce. Season. Split the naan bread open and fill it with the mixed filling.
2 Wrap in cling film and store in the fridge until ready to eat.

 Veggie swap

You could swap the beef for 50 g (1¾ oz) meat-free **Quorn Peppered Beef Style Slices** for 7 **ProPoints** values per serving.

 Cook's tip

You could also use the same amount of leftover roast beef from Sunday lunch for 9 **ProPoints** values per serving.

With this ideal take-to-work lunch, you'll avoid the supermarket's higher *ProPoints* value alternatives.

Coronation egg sandwich

 7 ProPoints value

Egg and 'bacon' roll

 8 ProPoints value

This vegetarian alternative is just as delicious as the classic version with chicken. The lightly spiced egg filling can be made a day ahead to save time in the morning.

Serves 1

15 minutes in total

7 ProPoints values per serving

7 ProPoints values per recipe

1 **egg**

½ teaspoon curry powder

1 tablespoon extra light mayonnaise

2 slices wholemeal bread

a small handful of **watercress** leaves

salt and freshly ground black pepper

1 Put the egg in a small pan, cover with cold water and bring to the boil. Turn the heat down and cook the egg over a gentle boil for 8 minutes until hard boiled. Drain and cool the egg under cold running water.

2 Peel the egg and roughly chop it in a bowl. Stir the curry powder into the mayonnaise and season. Add to the egg and stir in.

3 Spoon the coronation egg on top of one slice of the bread. Put the watercress and the second slice of bread on top. Wrap in cling film and keep in the fridge until ready to eat.

 *Try this*

For traditional coronation chicken, swap the egg for 50 g (1¾ oz) chopped cold **skinless roast chicken** for 8 **ProPoints** values.

What's not to like about egg and bacon? This version comes with a twist!

Serves 1

15 minutes in total

8 ProPoints values per serving

8 ProPoints values per recipe

1 **egg**

2 turkey rashers

1 **tomato**, quartered, de-seeded and diced

1 teaspoon snipped **fresh chives**

1 wholemeal roll

1 teaspoon extra light mayonnaise

salt and freshly ground black pepper

1 Preheat the grill to medium high. Put the egg in a small saucepan, cover with cold water and bring to the boil. Turn the heat down slightly and cook over a gentle boil for 8 minutes until hard boiled. Drain and cool under cold running water. Peel the egg and roughly chop in a bowl.

2 Meanwhile, cook the turkey rashers under the grill for 1½ minutes on each side. Leave to cool and cut in half crossways.

3 Add the tomato and most of the chives to the bowl with the egg and mix them together. Season.

4 Split the roll in half and spread with the mayonnaise. Top with the turkey rashers and the egg mixture. Sprinkle with a few extra chives. Top with the second half of the roll, wrap in cling film and chill until ready to serve.

V *Veggie swap*

For a meat-free alternative, use two rashers of vegetarian bacon instead of the turkey rashers. Cook as described in the recipe above for the same **ProPoints** values.

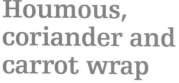

Houmous, coriander and carrot wrap

You could add a chopped, dried ready-to-eat date to the filling, if you like, for an extra 1 *ProPoints* value per serving.

Serves 1
5 minutes in total
5 *ProPoints* values per serving
5 *ProPoints* values per recipe

40 g (1½ oz) wholemeal tortilla wrap
3 teaspoons reduced fat houmous
1 small **carrot**, peeled and grated
a few baby **spinach** leaves
a squeeze of lemon juice
a large pinch of ground coriander
salt and freshly ground black pepper

1 Heat a dry non stick frying pan. When hot, add the tortilla and warm for a few moments. (This makes it easier to fold.) Remove from the pan, then set to one side.
2 Spread the houmous over the tortilla and top with the carrot and spinach. Add the lemon juice and sprinkle over the coriander. Season, then fold in the sides of the tortilla. Roll up the tortilla and wrap in cling film until ready to eat.

More to spend?
A chopped, hard boiled **egg** makes a filling addition to this wrap for an extra 2 *ProPoints* values.

Tricolore wrap

They say simple things are the best, and that certainly applies to this wrap with its Italian-inspired filling.

Serves 1
10 minutes in total
6 *ProPoints* values per serving
6 *ProPoints* values per recipe

40 g (1½ oz) wholemeal tortilla wrap
25 g (1 oz) Parma ham
a few soft **lettuce leaves**
1 **tomato**, sliced
40 g (1½ oz) light mozzarella, drained, patted dry, and torn into pieces
6 large **fresh basil** leaves
freshly ground black pepper

1 Heat a dry non stick frying pan. When hot, add the tortilla and warm for a few moments. (This makes it easier to fold.) Remove from the pan, then set to one side. Add the Parma ham to the pan and cook for 2 minutes, turning once, until just crisp.
2 Put the lettuce, tomato, mozzarella and basil on top of the tortilla. Season with black pepper, then put the warmed Parma ham on top. Fold in the sides and roll up. Slice in half horizontally and chill, wrapped in cling film. Bring up to room temperature before eating.

Fancy a bit extra?
Follow this tasty wrap with a refreshing 125 g pot of low fat fruit fromage frais for an extra 3 *ProPoints* values.

Pastrami and coleslaw on rye

It's best to throw this together just before you want it, but the coleslaw can be made ahead of time to make it easy to assemble. Since it's difficult to make coleslaw in small quantities for one, this recipe makes enough for two servings so you can use half and store half for later.

Serves 1

10 minutes in total

9 *ProPoints* values per serving

9 *ProPoints* values per recipe

2 x 50 g (1¾ oz) slices German rye bread

4 slices pastrami, about 50 g (1¾ oz) in total

For the coleslaw

1 large **carrot**, peeled and grated coarsely

50 g (1¾ oz) red **cabbage**, grated coarsely

3 tablespoons **virtually fat free plain yogurt**

1 teaspoon lemon juice

1 teaspoon wholegrain mustard

salt and freshly ground black pepper

1 To make the coleslaw, mix together all the ingredients for the coleslaw in a bowl and season. Divide the coleslaw in half and store one half in the fridge for another time. Divide the remaining coleslaw between the two slices of rye bread.

2 Just before serving, top each slice of rye bread with two slices of pastrami.

Veggie swap

For a vegetarian option, replace the pastrami with the same weight of **Quorn Peppered Beef Style Slices** for the same ***ProPoints*** values.

More to spend?

For afters, follow this with a slice of Weight Watchers malt loaf for an extra 2 ***ProPoints*** values. Top with a chopped small **banana**, for no extra ***ProPoints*** values.

Enjoy planning your lunches in advance and make it part of your regular routine.

Mini ham quiches

These clever pastry-free quiches go well with a large **mixed leaf** and **tomato** salad for no extra **ProPoints** values per serving.

Serves 2
Preparation time 10 minutes
Cooking time 15 minutes
6 ProPoints values per serving
12 ProPoints values per recipe

calorie controlled cooking spray
8 x 15 g (½ oz) **premium ham** slices
4 **eggs**
3 tablespoons **skimmed milk**
4 stalks **fresh chives**
salt and freshly ground black pepper

1 Preheat the oven to Gas Mark 5/190°C/fan oven 170°C. Spray four holes of a deep muffin tin with the cooking spray. Stack two slices of ham on top of each other, then gather up the edges and pop into one of the holes in the muffin tray. Press the ham out to make a 'case' – it doesn't matter if it gathers slightly in places. Repeat with the remaining ham.

2 Beat together the eggs and milk in a jug and season with a little salt and a generous amount of pepper. Pour the mixture carefully into the ham cases until it almost comes to the top. Snip over the chives.

3 Bake the quiches for about 15 minutes until the filling is just firm. Leave to cool in the tin, then ease out each quiche using a knife. Serve two quiches each.

 Take to work tip

To transport these, be sure to wrap them carefully in foil so they survive the journey well.

More to spend?

Enjoy these with a 35 g (1¼ oz) slice of crusty granary bread for an extra 4 **ProPoints** values per serving.

Put the ham into the holes of the muffin tin.

Pour the beaten egg and milk into the ham cases.

Snip the chives over each quiche before baking.

Tuna and white bean crostini

Serve this creamy tuna dip with sticks of **carrot, cucumber**, red **pepper** and **celery** for no extra *ProPoints* values.

Serves 2
10 minutes in total
7 *ProPoints* values per serving
15 *ProPoints* values per recipe

60 g (2 oz) canned **butter beans in water**, drained
80 g (3 oz) can **tuna in spring water**, drained
2 **spring onions**, chopped finely
juice of a small lemon
1 tablespoon extra light mayonnaise
1 teaspoon olive oil
salt and freshly ground black pepper
6 x 20 g (¾ oz) slices French bread, to serve

1 Put the butter beans, tuna, the white part of the spring onion, lemon juice, mayonnaise and olive oil in a blender with 1 tablespoon of water. Blend to a fairly smooth paste. You could also use a hand blender to do this but you may have to blend it in two batches.
2 Season the dip, then transfer it to a bowl and scatter over the green part of the spring onions.
3 Lightly toast the slices of French bread. Leave to cool. To serve, place three slices of toast on each plate, and spoon the dip on top of the toasts.

 Take to work tip

If you're taking this to work, once the bread is cool in Step 3, wrap it in cling film until ready to eat. Divide the tuna and white bean dip between two lidded containers and chill until ready to enjoy.

Prawn cocktail pitta

It's so easy to make prawn cocktail and it tastes so much better than the shop-bought version.

Serves 1
5 minutes in total
7 *ProPoints* values per serving
7 *ProPoints* values per recipe

75 g (2¾ oz) frozen cooked peeled **prawns**, defrosted
1 tablespoon extra light mayonnaise
1 teaspoon tomato ketchup
a squeeze of lemon juice
5 drops of Tabasco
1 wholemeal pitta bread, about 60 g (2 oz)
2 Little Gem **lettuce leaves**
salt and freshly ground black pepper
1 lemon wedge, to serve

1 Mix together the prawns, mayonnaise, ketchup, lemon juice and Tabasco in a bowl and season.
2 Carefully open the pitta bread out to make a pocket. Put the lettuce leaves inside the pitta and spoon in the prawn cocktail. Wrap in cling film and chill until ready to eat. Serve with the lemon wedge.

 Try this

You could serve the prawn cocktail mixture as part of a salad on top of a bed of shredded **lettuce** and **watercress** sprigs, accompanied by 100 g (3½ oz) boiled new **potatoes**, for 5 *ProPoints* values.

Smoked trout salad

This main meal salad comes with a herby mayonnaise dressing. To save time in the morning, it's best to cook the potatoes the day before, then leave them to cool overnight.

Serves 1
Preparation time 10 minutes
Cooking time 15 minutes
6 ProPoints values per serving
6 ProPoints values per recipe

100 g (3½ oz) new **potatoes**, halved or quartered, depending on size

4 soft **lettuce leaves**

1 **carrot**, peeled and grated

3 thin slices of red **onion**, rings separated

1 large cooked **beetroot**, diced

65 g (2¼ oz) cooked **skinless smoked trout fillet**, broken into large flakes

For the dressing

1 tablespoon extra light mayonnaise

2 teaspoons lemon juice

1 tablespoon chopped **fresh dill** (optional)

salt and freshly ground black pepper

1 Put the potatoes in a medium lidded saucepan, cover with cold water and bring to the boil, covered. Reduce the heat and simmer for 12–15 minutes until tender, then drain well and leave to cool. This can be done the night before.

2 Put the lettuce in the bottom of a lidded container, then top with the carrot, red onion, beetroot, trout and potatoes. Cover with the lid and store in the fridge.

3 Mix together the ingredients for the dressing with 1 tablespoon of water. Season the dressing and put it in a separate small lidded pot.

4 Chill the salad and dressing until ready to eat. Just before serving, spoon the dressing over the salad.

 Veggie swap

For a vegetarian alternative, omit the trout and top the salad with 1 hard boiled **egg**, cut into quarters, for 5 **ProPoints** values. Cool the egg under cold running water after cooking, then peel and slice just before serving.

 Try this

Why not make this salad with 50 g (1¾ oz) cooked **skinless chicken breast** instead of the trout, for 5 **ProPoints** values?

Tuna pasta

This delicioius pasta dish is quick and nutritious – just what you need on a busy day.

Serves 2
20 minutes in total
7 *ProPoints* values per serving
14 *ProPoints* values per recipe

100 g (3½ oz) dried **wholewheat penne**
1 teaspoon olive oil
2 **garlic cloves**, chopped
200 ml (7 fl oz) **passata**
2 teaspoons tomato ketchup
½ teaspoon dried oregano
a pinch of sugar
80 g (3 oz) can **tuna steak in spring water**, drained
salt and freshly ground black pepper
fresh basil leaves, to garnish

1 Bring a medium saucepan of water to the boil and cook the pasta according to the packet instructions, for about 10 minutes or until al dente, then drain, reserving 1 tablespoon of the cooking water.

2 While the pasta is cooking, heat the olive oil and garlic in a medium lidded saucepan for 30 seconds, stirring. Stir in the passata, ketchup, oregano and sugar. Bring to the boil, then turn the heat down to medium low, part-cover the pan, and simmer for 8 minutes, stirring the sauce occasionally.

3 Add the tuna to the tomato sauce and stir, breaking the fish up slightly into chunks with the spoon. Cook for another 3 minutes, stirring occasionally. Add the pasta and reserved cooking water, mix thoroughly, then season to taste.

4 Leave the tuna pasta to cool then divide between two lidded containers. Reheat before serving and garnish with the basil leaves.

With a little planning ahead, you can have a filling and warming lunch and keep to your *ProPoints* allowance.

Chicken and pesto pasta salad

A spoonful of pesto adds a real lift to this summery salad.

Serves 2
20 minutes in total
6 *ProPoints* values per serving
13 *ProPoints* values per recipe

75 g (2¾ oz) dried orzo pasta or other small pasta shapes
100 g (3½ oz) cooked **skinless chicken breast**, cut into small pieces
10 cherry **tomatoes**, quartered
3 teaspoons extra light mayonnaise
2 teaspoons reduced fat pesto
1 teaspoon lemon juice
2 handfuls of **rocket** leaves
salt and freshly ground black pepper

1 Bring a medium saucepan of water to the boil and cook the pasta according to the packet instructions for about 8 minutes or until al dente. Drain, rinse under cold running water and drain again.
2 Transfer the pasta to a bowl with the chicken and tomatoes.
3 To make the dressing, mix together the mayonnaise, pesto and lemon juice. Season the dressing and spoon it over the pasta mixture.
4 Divide the rocket leaves between two lidded containers. Spoon the pasta mixture on top and cover with lids. Store in the fridge until ready to eat.

 Veggie swap

This is a versatile pasta salad and can be adapted in many ways. For a vegetarian version, replace the chicken with 25 g (1 oz) canned **chick peas in water**, drained, per person for 5 *ProPoints* values per serving.

 Super quick

Chicken tikka salad with sweet chilli dressing

Assemble this salad in the morning, but don't stir in the tangy dressing until just before serving. Serve with a 60 g (2 oz) wholemeal pitta bread for an extra **4 *ProPoints*** values.

Serves 1
10 minutes in total
2 *ProPoints* values per serving
2 *ProPoints* values per recipe

2 large handfuls of mixed **salad** leaves
3 thin slices of red **onion**, separated
1 small **carrot**, peeled and grated
5 **radishes**, sliced
4 cm (1½ inches) **cucumber**, quartered, de-seeded and diced
100 g (3½ oz) cooked chicken tikka slices

For the sweet chilli dressing
2 teaspoons lime juice
1 teaspoon sweet chilli sauce
salt and freshly ground black pepper

1 To make the dressing, mix the lime juice and sweet chilli sauce with 1–2 teaspoons of water to make a runny, sauce-like consistency. Season and transfer to a lidded pot.
2 Put the salad leaves, red onions, carrot, radishes and cucumber in a separate lidded container. Wrap the chicken in cling film and add it to the container.
3 Before eating, toss the salad in the dressing and top with the chicken, discarding the cling film.

Super quick

Asian beef and lettuce wrap

This aromatic beef wrap is filled with delicious roast beef and crunchy vegetables, then topped off with a fantastic sauce for dipping or drizzling.

Serves 1

10 minutes in total

6 ProPoints values per serving

6 ProPoints values per recipe

4 **fresh basil** leaves

1 Romaine **lettuce leaf**

35 g (1¼ oz) cooked roast beef, sliced into long strips

½ red **pepper**, de-seeded, halved and cut into long strips

5 cm (2 inches) **cucumber**, de-seeded and cut into long strips

1 **spring onion**, cut into long strips

42 g soft tortilla wrap

For the dipping sauce

1 tablespoon sweet chilli sauce or plum sauce

juice of ½ a lime

1 teaspoon light soy sauce

1 Mix together the ingredients for the dipping sauce in a small bowl.

2 Put the basil leaves on top of the lettuce leaf and top with strips of beef, red pepper, cucumber and spring onion. Roll up in the tortilla wrap and drizzle over the sauce or dip the tortilla into the sauce before eating.

 Try this

You can also make this recipe with 60 g (2 oz) cooked peeled **prawns** instead of the beef, for the same **ProPoints** values.

 Make ahead

If you're taking this to work, put the vegetables and beef in a lidded container. Mix together the ingredients for the dipping sauce in a small lidded pot and wrap the tortilla in cling film. Assemble as described in the method above when ready to serve.

Japanese chicken noodle salad

A complete meal-in-a-pot, this salad is just as good eaten hot or cold. To serve warm, mix the spinach leaves into the noodles, then microwave until heated through.

Serves 2

15 minutes in total

6 *ProPoints* values per serving

12 *ProPoints* values per recipe

75 g (2¾ oz) dried wholewheat noodles

1 **carrot**, peeled and cut into 3 chunks, then each chunk cut into fine strips

3 **spring onions**, sliced thinly

½ red **pepper**, de-seeded and sliced thinly

90 g (3¼ oz) cooked **skinless chicken breast**, shredded

2 handfuls of baby **spinach** leaves

a small handful of **fresh basil** leaves

For the miso dressing

1 tablespoon instant miso soup (see Cook's tip)

¼ kettleful of boiling water

½ teaspoon toasted sesame oil

a pinch of dried chilli flakes (optional)

1 Bring a medium saucepan of water to the boil and cook the noodles according to the packet instructions, then drain and rinse under cold running water. Leave to drain.

2 To make the dressing, mix the instant miso with 4 tablespoons of boiing water. Stir in the sesame oil and chilli flakes, if using, and set to one side.

3 Put the noodles in a large bowl with the carrot, spring onions, red pepper and chicken. Pour the dressing over the top and turn until everything is coated.

4 Put a bed of spinach leaves in each lidded container. Divide the noodle salad between the containers and top with the basil leaves, then cover with the lids. Store in the fridge until ready to eat.

 Cook's tip

Miso can be bought either as a thick paste or in powdered form. The paste will keep for months, stored in the fridge. A spoonful makes an instant soup or can be added to stews, dressings and sauces. Powdered instant miso is sold in sachets and needs to be mixed with hot water before using. You can substitute 2 tablespoons of miso paste for the instant miso soup here.

Fattoush with chorizo

Bright, vibrant and full of flavour, this Moroccan-style salad makes a complete meal. It's best served at room temperature, so try to remove it from the fridge 30 minutes before serving. The pitta should be added just before you serve.

Serves 2

20 minutes in total

5 *ProPoints* values per serving

10 *ProPoints* values per recipe

50 g (1¾ oz) diced chorizo

1 wholemeal pitta bread, halved

½ teaspoon cumin seeds

4 **tomatoes**, cut into chunks

10 cm (4 inches) **cucumber**, quartered lengthways, de-seeded and cut into chunks

1 small red **pepper**, de-seeded and cut into rings

½ red **onion**, cut into rings

3 sprigs **fresh mint**, leaves removed and torn

3 sprigs **fresh flat leaf parsley**, leaves removed and torn

For the yogurt dressing

4 tablespoons **virtually fat free plain yogurt**

1 tablespoon lemon juice

1 small **garlic clove**, crushed

salt and freshly ground black pepper

1 Put the chorizo in a dry non stick frying pan over a medium heat. Cook for 3 minutes, turning occasionally, until crisp all over. Remove from the pan and drain on a paper towel.

2 Meanwhile, carefully split each pitta half open. Wipe the pan clean and add the pitta bread, then toast for 3 minutes, turning once, until starting to crisp. Remove from the pan and leave to cool.

3 Put the cumin seeds in the pan and toast for 30 seconds until they begin to smell aromatic. Remove from the pan and set to one side.

4 Divide the tomatoes, cucumber, red pepper, onion, mint and parsley between two lidded containers. Scatter the cumin and chorizo over the top. Wrap each pitta bread half in cling film. (If you are making the fattoush the night before, crisp the pitta in the morning.)

5 To make the dressing, mix together the yogurt, lemon juice, garlic and some seasoning. Divide between two small lidded pots. To serve, break the pitta bread into bite size pieces and scatter equally between the salads. Drizzle the dressing over and serve.

 Veggie swap

Light halloumi makes a great vegetarian alternative to the chorizo.

For two people, pat dry 50 g (1¾ oz) light halloumi and cut into small chunks. Spray a non stick frying pan with the cooking spray and cook the halloumi for 5 minutes until starting to turn golden. Leave to cool before sprinkling over the salad for the same ***ProPoints*** values per serving.

 Ingredient tip

Keep a ready supply of pitta bread by storing it in the freezer. It can be reheated from frozen in minutes under the grill or in a toaster.

Cook the chorizo in a
dry pan for 3 minutes.

Toast the pitta bread in
the pan until crisp.

Toast the cumin seeds
until they smell aromatic.

Meat free
nights

This *tasty* range of vegetarian suppers and light meals has something to *please* everyone in the family, helping you to better *manage* your food environment at home, so it works with your *weight loss* and not against it.

Summer minestrone with aioli

Fresh and vibrant, this soup is full of colour and flavour, and it makes the most of summery vegetables. A spoonful of the aioli (garlic mayonnaise) adds the finishing touch.

Serves 2

20 minutes in total

5 *ProPoints* values per serving

10 *ProPoints* values per recipe

60 g (2 oz) dried vermicelli or orzo pasta

600 ml (20 fl oz) vegetable stock

1 **carrot**, peeled and sliced thinly
   diagonally

1 small **fennel bulb**, sliced

1 bay leaf

3 **spring onions**, sliced thinly diagonally

60 g (2 oz) frozen **petit pois**

60 g (2 oz) **asparagus** tips

salt and freshly ground black pepper

For the aioli

1 tablespoon extra light mayonnaise

1 small **garlic clove**, crushed

To serve

a few **fresh basil** leaves (optional)

15 g (½ oz) Parmesan cheese, cut into
   fine shavings

1 Bring a medium saucepan of water to the boil and cook the vermicelli or orzo according to the packet instructions for about 8 minutes or until al dente. Drain and rinse under cold running water until cool. Drain again and set to one side.

2 While the pasta is cooking, pour the vegetable stock into a saucepan and bring to the boil. Add the carrot, fennel and bay leaf, then bring to a gentle simmer and cook for 4 minutes.

3 Add the spring onions, then add the petit pois and the asparagus. Return to a gentle simmer and cook for 2 minutes. Add the cooked pasta to the soup, season and cook for another minute or until the vegetables are tender.

4 To make the aioli, while the soup is cooking, mix together the mayonnaise and garlic in a small bowl.

5 Serve the soup topped with a spoonful of the aioli, sprinkled with the basil leaves, if using, and the Parmesan shavings.

 Try this

For a non vegetarian option, you could add 100 g (3½ oz) cooked peeled large **prawns** to the soup for 6 ***ProPoints*** values per serving. Add with the cooked orzo or vermicelli in Step 3 and heat through for 2 minutes.

Soup is the ideal
light meal.

Moroccan squash soup with crispy chick peas

This golden-coloured soup is delicious at any time of year but especially lovely and warming in the autumn. If you're dishing it up for the children too, don't use the chilli flakes.

Serves 4

40 minutes in total

1 ProPoints value per serving

4 ProPoints values per recipe

 (soup only)

calorie controlled cooking spray

2 **onions**, diced

2 **carrots**, peeled and sliced

800 g (1 lb 11 oz) **butternut squash**, peeled, de-seeded and diced

1 **celery** stick, sliced

1.2 litres (2 pints) vegetable stock

2 bay leaves

2.5 cm (1 inch) **fresh root ginger**, sliced into rounds (no need to peel)

a large pinch of chilli flakes (optional)

1 tablespoon ground coriander

1 teaspoon ground cumin

75 g (2¾ oz) canned **chick peas in water**, drained and rinsed

salt and freshly ground black pepper

2 tablespoons chopped **fresh coriander** leaves, to garnish

1 Heat a large lidded saucepan and spray with the cooking spray. Cook the onion for 5 minutes, covered, until softened. Add the carrots, butternut squash and celery, stir until combined, then pour in the stock.

2 Add the bay leaves, ginger, chilli flakes, if using, 1 teaspoon of the ground coriander and all the cumin to the pan. Bring to the boil, then reduce the heat, part-cover, and simmer for 20 minutes until the vegetables are tender.

3 While the soup is cooking, spray a large non stick frying pan with the cooking spray. Add the chick peas and cook for 10 minutes, shaking the pan occasionally until crisp. Add the remaining ground coriander, toss the chick peas until coated, then season with salt.

4 Divide the soup between four bowls and scatter the coriander and the crispy chick peas over the top. Season before serving.

 Freezing tip

This soup freezes really well. Leave to cool, then transfer to a large lidded container or divide into individual portions and freeze for up to 1 month.

Hungry family hint

A 26 g (1 oz) slice of garlic bread would really make a meal of this, for an additional 3 **ProPoints** values per serving.

If you're having dinner out, it's a great idea to plan the day's eating. Have a bowl of this soup at lunchtime and you won't arrive at the restaurant feeling famished.

Warm halloumi, pepper and lentil salad

Pepperdew peppers add a mild, sweet chilli heat as well as a touch of colour to this main meal salad. You can find these small red peppers in jars packed in vinegar in most supermarkets. This salad can also be served cold as part of a packed lunch.

Serves 2
20 minutes in total
7 ProPoints values per serving
13 ProPoints values per recipe
Ⓥ

400 g can **green lentils in water**, drained and rinsed
40 g (1½ oz) pepperdew peppers, drained and chopped or 1 medium size red **chilli**, de-seeded and sliced thinly
10 cherry **tomatoes**, halved
½ a small red **onion**, sliced thinly
juice of ½ a lemon
handful of **fresh basil** leaves, torn
handful of **fresh mint** leaves, chopped roughly
90 g (3¼ oz) light halloumi, patted dry
calorie controlled cooking spray
salt and freshly ground black pepper

1 Put the lentils, pepperdew peppers or chilli, tomatoes and red onion in a serving bowl. Squeeze the lemon juice over the top and season. Stir in the basil and mint leaves and set to one side, keeping the lentils at room temperature.

2 Heat a large, non stick griddle or frying pan over a high heat. Spray the pan and the halloumi with the cooking spray and griddle or fry for about 3 minutes, turning once, until golden in places. Remove the halloumi from the pan, break into pieces and scatter over the top of the salad. Serve while the halloumi is still warm.

👉 Try this

Instead of the halloumi, you could top each serving with a soft boiled **egg**, halved, for 5 **ProPoints** values per serving. Or for a more substantial non vegetarian supper, why not serve the salad as an accompaniment to a griddled 150 g (5½ oz) **skinless boneless chicken breast** per person, in place of the halloumi, for the same **ProPoints** values per serving?

Pear, polenta and soft cheese salad

Honey-coated pears, crisp polenta, soft cheese and crunchy nuts make a perfect combination in this large salad.

Serves 2

25 minutes in total

8 *ProPoints* values per serving

17 *ProPoints* values per recipe

V

15 g (½ oz) walnut halves

calorie controlled cooking spray

75 g (2¾ oz) ready-made polenta, cubed

2 ripe but not too soft **pears**, peeled, cored and cut into wedges

1 teaspoon clear honey

½ teaspoon ground ginger

60 g (2 oz) **spinach**, **watercress** and **rocket** salad

1 large cooked **beetroot**, cut into bite size pieces

1–2 teaspoons lemon juice, to taste

40 g (1½ oz) low fat soft cheese

salt and freshly ground black pepper

1 Toast the walnuts in a dry, non stick frying pan for 3 minutes, over a medium heat, turning once, or until slightly browned. Remove from the pan, roughly chop and set to one side.

2 Return the frying pan to the medium heat. Spray with the cooking spray and fry the polenta, turning regularly, for 4–5 minutes until it is golden all over. Remove from the pan and set to one side.

3 Put the pears in the pan, spray with more cooking spray, and cook over a medium heat for 2 minutes, turning once, until starting to soften. Add the honey, ginger and 1 tablespoon of water and cook, turning once, for another 2 minutes, until light golden and sticky.

4 Divide the salad leaves between two serving plates, top with the pear and the beetroot and drizzle the lemon juice over, to taste. Season and top the salad with the polenta, walnuts and little dollops of the soft cheese.

More to spend?

This would be great with a 50 g (1¾ oz) crusty bread roll per person for an extra 4 ***ProPoints*** values per serving, or two 13 g (½ oz) oatcakes per person for an extra 3 ***ProPoints*** values per serving.

Cherry tomato tarte tatin

This easy, summery tart goes really well with a **rocket, spinach and watercress** salad.

Serves 4
Preparation time 15 minutes
Cooking time 25 minutes
5 *ProPoints* values per serving
19 *ProPoints* values per recipe

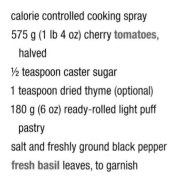

calorie controlled cooking spray
575 g (1 lb 4 oz) cherry **tomatoes**, halved
½ teaspoon caster sugar
1 teaspoon dried thyme (optional)
180 g (6 oz) ready-rolled light puff pastry
salt and freshly ground black pepper
fresh basil leaves, to garnish

1 Preheat the oven to Gas Mark 7/220°C/fan oven 200°C. Spray the base and sides of a 20 cm (8 inch) round, non stick baking tin with the cooking spray. Arrange the tomatoes over the base of the tin, cut sides facing upwards. They should be tightly packed together and cover the whole base of the tin. Spray the tomatoes with the cooking spray and sprinkle with the sugar and thyme, if using, then season.

2 Trim the pastry to fit the 20 cm (8 inch) tin, leaving a 1 cm (½ inch) border. Lay the pastry carefully over the tomatoes and tuck in the edges, down the sides of the tin. Bake for 20 minutes until risen and golden. Remove from the oven and put a plate on top of the tin. Wearing oven gloves, carefully turn the tart out of the tin on to the plate. Slip the tart on to a baking sheet and bake for another 5 minutes until the pastry is cooked and the tomatoes are tender.

3 Season, scatter the basil over the top of the tart and serve, cut into wedges.

Hungry family hint

This is even more filling with 150 g (5½ oz) of boiled new **potatoes** per person for an extra 3 ***ProPoints*** values per serving.

Arrange the tomatoes cut side up in the tin.

Lay the pastry carefully over the tomatoes.

Tuck in the pastry edges, down the sides of the tin.

Here's the perfect light supper for when you want something in the evening that won't spend a lot of your *ProPoints* budget.

Fusilli with creamy mushroom ragout

This creamy mixed mushroom and spinach sauce with pasta makes a complete supper. Here, it comes with fusilli, but you could try it with any of your favourite pasta shapes.

Serves 4

40 minutes in total

8 ProPoints values per serving

33 ProPoints values per recipe

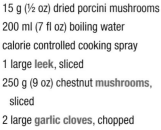

15 g (½ oz) dried porcini mushrooms

200 ml (7 fl oz) boiling water

calorie controlled cooking spray

1 large **leek**, sliced

250 g (9 oz) chestnut **mushrooms**, sliced

2 large **garlic cloves**, chopped

1 **courgette**, sliced

1 teaspoon dried thyme

240 g (8½ oz) dried fusilli

200 ml (7 fl oz) dry white wine (see Tip)

150 g (5½ oz) low fat soft cheese

100 g (3½ oz) **spinach**

salt and freshly ground black pepper

1 Soak the porcini mushrooms in the boiled water for 20 minutes, until softened, then strain, reserving the soaking liquid to use in Step 5. Using the back of a spoon, squeeze out any excess water from the mushrooms, then roughly chop them.

2 Heat a large, deep, lidded, non stick frying pan over a medium heat. Spray with the cooking spray and cook the leek for 3 minutes, covered, until softened. Stir the leek occasionally. Add the porcini and chestnut mushrooms, garlic, courgette and thyme and cook for 5 minutes until softened.

3 Bring a large saucepan of water to the boil and cook the pasta according to the packet instructions for about 10 minutes until al dente, then drain, reserving 2 tablespoons of the cooking water for the sauce.

4 Meanwhile, pour the wine into the mushroom mixture and let it bubble for about 2 minutes, uncovered, until it has reduced and there is no smell of alcohol.

5 Reduce the heat to low. Stir the low fat soft cheese, spinach, reserved water from the pasta and reserved soaking liquid into the sauce. Return the lid and cook for another 2 minutes until the spinach has wilted. Top the pasta with the sauce, season and serve.

 Ingredient tips

• Dried porcini mushrooms are a fabulous addition to the store cupboard. Not only do they keep for months, but just a little adds tons of flavour to stews, pasta sauces, soups and stir-fries.

• Instead of wine, you can also use the same amount of vegetable stock for 7 **ProPoints** values per serving.

Spring vegetable pasta with crispy crumbs

Garlicky and lemony golden crumbs add a tasty crunch when sprinkled over this Mediterranean-style pasta dish.

Serves 2

25 minutes in total

8 *ProPoints* values per serving

16 *ProPoints* values per recipe

125 g (4½ oz) dried tagliatelle pasta

75 g (2¾ oz) **asparagus** tips, trimmed

1 **courgette**, cut lengthways into long, thin slices

15 g (½ oz) fresh breadcrumbs

calorie controlled cooking spray

1 **garlic clove**, chopped finely

juice and finely grated zest of ½ a lemon

4 **spring onions**, sliced

8 vine ripened cherry **tomatoes**, quartered

1 teaspoon olive oil

40 g (1½ oz) low fat soft cheese

salt and freshly ground black pepper

fresh basil leaves, to garnish (optional)

1 Bring a large saucepan of water to the boil and cook the pasta according to the packet instructions for about 10 minutes until al dente. Drain, reserving 5 tablespoons of the cooking water.

2 While the pasta is cooking, cook the asparagus and courgette in boiling water for 3–4 minutes until just tender. Refresh under cold running water to cool, then set to one side.

3 Heat a large, non stick frying pan over a medium heat, add the breadcrumbs, spray with the cooking spray and cook for about 3 minutes until beginning to turn crisp. Add the garlic, spray again with the cooking spray and cook for another minute, stirring. Remove from the heat, then transfer to a bowl and stir in the lemon zest. Set to one side until ready to use. Wipe the pan clean.

4 Spray the pan with the cooking spray. Fry the spring onions and tomatoes for 3 minutes until softened. Remove the pan from the heat and add the pasta, asparagus, courgette, reserved cooking water, olive oil and lemon juice. Season and turn until everything is combined, then set the pan over a medium-low heat until heated through.

5 Serve the pasta, topped with small dollops of the soft cheese and sprinkled with the breadcrumbs. Scatter over a few basil leaves, if you like.

 *Make ahead*

The crispy crumbs can be made up to 3 days ahead if cooled and stored in an airtight container.

Family friendly

Oven baked tomato risotto with Parmesan crisps

The beauty of this risotto is that is doesn't need lots of stirring – instead this one-pot meal is cooked in the oven. The cheese crisps have a lovely intense flavour, but you can stir the Parmesan into the risotto just before serving instead, if you prefer.

Serves 4

Preparation time 25 minutes

Cooking time 40 minutes

6 ProPoints values per serving

25 ProPoints values per recipe

 (excluding Parmesan crisps)

calorie controlled cooking spray

2 **onions**, chopped finely

200 g (7 oz) dried risotto rice

2 **courgettes**, diced

3 large **garlic cloves**, chopped

25 g (1 oz) Parmesan cheese, grated finely

6 tablespoons red wine or extra stock

300 ml (10 fl oz) hot vegetable stock

400 g can chopped **tomatoes**

1 teaspoon tomato purée

1 teaspoon dried oregano

salt and freshly ground black pepper

1 Preheat the oven to Gas Mark 4/180°C/fan oven 160°C. Heat a large, tight-lidded, ovenproof saucepan or flameproof casserole dish. Spray with the cooking spray and cook the onions, covered, for 8 minutes until softened. Stir the onions occasionally.

2 Add the risotto rice, courgettes and garlic. Spray again with the cooking spray, and cook for another 2 minutes until the courgettes have softened.

3 Meanwhile, to make the Parmesan crisps, line a baking sheet with non stick baking paper. Sprinkle 1 tablespoon of the Parmesan into a mound on the baking sheet. Tidy the edges slightly to make a round about 4 cm (1½ inches) in diameter, then repeat to make four rounds in total, spacing them out on the baking sheet. Bake for 6–8 minutes until golden and crisp. Leave to cool for a few minutes, then lift them off the baking paper with a palette knife. Set aside.

4 While the Parmesan crisps are cooking, add the wine to the risotto and cook, stirring until it is absorbed by the rice. Add the stock, chopped tomatoes, tomato purée and oregano. Season, then stir well until combined.

5 Cover the risotto and bake for 35–40 minutes, until the rice is tender, stirring halfway through. Remove from the oven and set aside, covered, for 5 minutes. Serve the risotto in bowls, each topped with a Parmesan crisp.

Cook's tips

• If you ever have any leftover wine, it's well worth freezing it in ice cube size portions, for up to 1 month, for future use in sauces or stews.

• Rice dishes can be frozen for up to 1 month, but it's important to defrost them fully before reheating, then heat through thoroughly until piping hot.

Add the risotto rice, courgettes and garlic.

Sprinkle 1 tbsp of cheese per crisp on a lined baking sheet.

Lift the Parmesan crisps off with a palette knife.

Leek, pea and mint risotto

This risotto is flavoured with a minty pea purée, then served with a softly poached egg – delicious!

Serves 4

45 minutes in total

8 *ProPoints* values per serving

34 *ProPoints* values per recipe

V ❄ (risotto only)

calorie controlled cooking spray

2 large **leeks**, sliced

300 g (10½ oz) frozen **petit pois**

850 ml (1½ pints) hot vegetable stock

10 g (¼ oz) **fresh mint** leaves plus
   extra, to garnish

200 g (7 oz) dried risotto rice

125 ml (4 fl oz) dry white wine

4 **eggs**

freshly ground black pepper

1   Heat a large lidded saucepan over a medium heat. Spray with the cooking spray and fry the leeks for 5 minutes, stirring regularly, until softened.

2   Meanwhile, put the petit pois in a medium size saucepan and cover with 100 ml (3½ fl oz) of the stock. Bring to the boil, then reduce the heat and simmer for 3 minutes until tender. Remove from the heat, add the mint and blend to a coarse purée, using a hand blender, then set aside.

3   Add the rice to the pan with the leeks and stir until combined, then cook, stirring, for 2 minutes. Pour in the wine and cook, stirring, until it is absorbed by the rice. Start to add the hot stock a ladleful at a time, stirring constantly. Continue adding the stock until the rice is tender. It will take 20–25 minutes. If the rice is not quite tender once all the stock has been added, add a little hot water and stir a little longer. When the rice is ready, stir in the pea purée and heat through for 2 minutes. Remove from the heat, cover, and leave to stand while you poach the eggs.

4   To poach the eggs, fill a large, deep frying pan with warm water until three-quarters full. Bring the water almost to boiling point. Turn down the heat to a gentle simmer. Crack one of the eggs into a ramekin and slip the egg gently into the pan of simmering water. Repeat with the remaining eggs and poach them all for 3–4 minutes until the white is set but the yolk remains a little runny. Remove the eggs from the water with a slotted spoon and drain briefly on kitchen towel.

5   Season with black pepper and serve the risotto in bowls, topped with a poached egg each and garnished with mint leaves.

 Ingredient tip

Instead of the wine, you can also use the same amount of vegetable stock for 7 ***ProPoints*** values per serving.

Hungry family hint

Top with an extra poached egg per person for an additional 2 ***ProPoints*** values per serving. You could also serve the risotto with a 40 g (1½ oz) slice of ciabatta bread per person for an extra 3 ***ProPoints*** values per serving.

Risotto is a family favourite which means you can relax and enjoy this meal together and still stay within your *ProPoints* allowance.

Mushroom Wellington

This is a great vegetarian alternative to the classic beef Wellington and makes a delicious meat-free option for a Sunday lunch.

Serves 4

Preparation time 25 minutes

Cooking time 40 minutes

8 *ProPoints* values per serving

31 *ProPoints* values per recipe

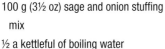

100 g (3½ oz) sage and onion stuffing
   mix

½ a kettleful of boiling water

3 **carrots**, peeled and sliced

4 large portobello or field **mushrooms**,
   stalks removed

calorie controlled cooking spray

4 teaspoons redcurrant jelly

6 x 45 g sheets Jus-Rol filo pastry,
   each measuring 50 x 24 cm
   (20 x 9½ inches), defrosted if frozen

freshly ground black pepper

1 Put the stuffing mix in a heatproof bowl and pour 250 ml (9 fl oz) boiling water over. Stir well and leave for 10–15 minutes, covered with a plate, until the stuffing has absorbed the water. Give it a good stir and set to one side.

2 Meanwhile, boil the carrots until tender. Transfer them to a bowl and mash with the back of a fork to make a coarse purée. Stir the carrot into the stuffing mixture.

3 Spray both sides of each mushroom with the cooking spray and place each one cap-side down on a chopping board or plate. Spread a teaspoon of the redcurrant jelly over the underside (gills) of each mushroom. Divide the stuffing mixture between the mushrooms, piling it on top. Season with black pepper.

4 Preheat the oven to Gas Mark 6/180°C/fan oven 160°C. Cut each sheet of filo in half horizontally, to make 12 squares in total. Place three halves of filo on top of each other, spraying each layer with the cooking spray. Sit a mushroom in the centre. Draw up the corners of the filo to meet in the middle and make a parcel. Twist the top of the filo to seal and spray the parcel with more cooking spray. Repeat with the remaining stuffed mushrooms and filo halves to make your parcels.

5 Spray a non stick baking tray with the cooking spray and place the mushroom parcels on it. Bake for 35–40 minutes until the filo is golden and crisp.

 Cook's tip

When making the parcels, it's best to cover any filo that you aren't using with a damp tea towel, to prevent it from drying out.

 *Make ahead*

The stuffing and carrot mixture can be made up to 3 days in advance and kept covered in the fridge until ready to use. Bring the stuffing and carrot mixture to room temperature before stuffing the mushrooms.

Pile the stuffing on top of the mushrooms.

Sit a mushroom in the middle of the filo squares.

Draw up the corners of the filo to make a parcel.

Roasted vegetable pizza

 7 ProPoints value

Topped with colourful roasted vegetables, this thin-crust pizza can also be sprinkled with 60 g (2 oz) stoned black olives for no extra *ProPoints* values per serving.

Serves 4

Preparation time 30 minutes

Cooking time 25 minutes

7 *ProPoints* values per serving

27 *ProPoints* values per recipe

 (uncooked base only)

calorie controlled cooking spray

2 red **onions**, halved crossways and
  each half cut into four wedges

1 red **pepper**, de-seeded and cut into
  6 long pieces

1 yellow **pepper**, de-seeded and cut
  into 6 long pieces

2 **courgettes**, sliced

4 whole **garlic cloves**, unpeeled

75 g (2¾ oz) **passata with garlic and
  herbs**

8 cherry **tomatoes**

75 g (2¾ oz) light **mozzarella**, drained
  and torn into pieces

1 teaspoon olive oil

salt and freshly ground black pepper

a small handful of **fresh basil** leaves, to
  garnish (optional)

For the pizza base

200 g (7 oz) strong bread flour

½ teaspoon bicarbonate of soda

½ teaspoon salt

125 ml (4 fl oz) **virtually fat free plain
  yogurt**

1 tablespoon **skimmed milk**

1 Preheat the oven to Gas Mark 7/220°C/fan oven 200°C. Spray one large or two smaller non stick roasting tins with the cooking spray. Divide the onions, peppers, courgettes and garlic cloves between the tins. Spray with more cooking spray and roast for 10 minutes.

2 While the vegetables are roasting, make the pizza base. Mix together the flour (reserving 1 teaspoon for kneading), bicarbonate of soda and salt in a mixing bowl. Combine the yogurt and milk, then add to the flour mixture. Stir with a fork, then your fingers, to form it into a ball of dough. Knead briefly on a work surface, lightly floured with the reserved teaspoon of flour, until the dough is smooth.

3 Spray a large baking tray with the cooking spray. Roll out the dough to a rough 30 cm (12 inch) circle and place on the baking tray. Spoon the passata over the pizza base and spread it in an even layer, leaving a narrow border around the edge.

4 When the vegetables are ready, peel and halve the roasted garlic cloves, then put them on top of the pizza with the rest of the roasted vegetables and cherry tomatoes. Season, then spray the top with the cooking spray. Scatter over the mozzarella and drizzle with the olive oil, then bake for 20–25 minutes until the vegetables are tender and the mozzarella has melted and is golden in places. Serve, cut into wedges, sprinkled with basil leaves, if you like.

 *Cheat's tip*

Instead of making your own pizza base, try using a 290 g pizza base mix, for no extra *ProPoints* values. Make according to the packet instructions, then top as instructed in the recipe.

 Freezing tip

Why not make double the quantity of dough then freeze half, uncooked, and wrapped in cling film, to use another day? Defrost thoroughly before using, as above.

Add the yogurt and milk to the flour mixture.

Knead the dough briefly until it is smooth.

Scatter over the mozzarella cheese.

Have some fun in the kitchen – let your children make their own pizzas and choose their favourite toppings.

Posh beans on toast

To make this even more substantial, you could top the beans with a softly poached egg for an extra 2 *ProPoints* values per serving.

Serves 2

20 minutes in total

6 *ProPoints* values per serving

11 *ProPoints* values per recipe

V

calorie controlled cooking spray

4 large **spring onions**, sliced thinly

3 **garlic cloves**, chopped finely

250 g (9 oz) chestnut **mushrooms**, sliced

12 cherry **tomatoes**, halved

400 g can **butter beans in water**, drained and rinsed

200 g (7oz) baby **spinach** leaves

juice of a lemon

1 heaped teaspoon Dijon mustard

2 x 45 g (1½ oz) slices wholemeal bread

salt and freshly ground black pepper

1 Heat a large, deep, non stick frying pan over a medium heat. Spray with the cooking spray and fry the white part of the spring onions, garlic and mushrooms for 4 minutes, stirring occasionally, until softened.

2 Add the tomatoes and butter beans and cook for 3 minutes until heated through. Add the spinach, then remove from the heat briefly while you toss the ingredients together – it will look like a lot of spinach but it will all cook down eventually. You may need to add it in two batches.

3 Add the lemon juice and mustard, then cook for another 2–3 minutes until the spinach has wilted, before seasoning.

4 Meanwhile, toast the bread. Pile the butter bean mixture on top of the toast and serve straight away, sprinkled with the green part of the spring onions.

 Cook's tip

Cans of beans, such as **chick peas**, **kidney**, **haricot** and **cannellini**, make a great addition to the store cupboard. Have a few cans to hand for adding to stews, soups, or sauces, or to mash as an alternative to mashed potatoes.

 Try this

For a non vegetarian option, add 40 g (1½ oz) chopped chorizo to the frying pan with the spring onions in Step 1 for 9 *ProPoints* values per serving.

Here's the perfect light supper if you've had a big Sunday roast.

Mexican chilli beans with tortillas

Children will find it fun to make their own tortilla chips – and it's so easy to do too. This hearty stew is packed with delicious vegetables, as well as some filling beans, to keep the whole family feeling satisfied for longer.

Serves 4

30 minutes in total

7 ProPoints values per serving

28 ProPoints values per recipe

  (chilli beans only)

calorie controlled cooking spray

1 large **onion**, chopped

4 **garlic cloves**, chopped

150 g (5½ oz) **mushrooms**, chopped

1 red **pepper**, de-seeded and chopped

1 **courgette**, sliced

400 g can chopped **tomatoes**

6 tablespoons vegetable stock

400 g can **mixed beans in water**, drained and rinsed

1 teaspoon smoked paprika or regular paprika

2 teaspoons ground cumin

2 teaspoons dried thyme

4 x 40 g (1½ oz) wholewheat tortillas

4 tablespoons reduced fat houmous

salt and freshly ground black pepper

1 Heat a large, lidded saucepan and spray with the cooking spray. Cook the onion over a medium heat for 5 minutes, covered, until softened. Add the garlic, mushrooms, red pepper and courgette, spray with more cooking spray and fry, covered, for another 5 minutes until softened.

2 Add the tomatoes, stock, mixed beans, paprika, cumin and thyme and bring to the boil. Turn the heat down to low and simmer, stirring occasionally, for 15 minutes until the sauce has reduced and thickened, then season.

3 While the chilli beans are cooking, heat the oven to Gas Mark 6/200°C/fan oven 180°C. Cut each tortilla into 12 wedges, put on a baking tray and bake for 4–5 minutes until crisp. Remove from the oven and keep warm.

4 Serve the chilli beans in shallow bowls, topped with a spoonful of houmous and with the tortilla wedges.

 Try this

For a non vegetarian option, add 150 g (5½ oz) cooked **skinless chicken breast fillet** to the chilli beans in Step 2 for an extra 2 **ProPoints** values per serving. Heat through for 5 minutes.

 Freezing tip

The Mexican chilli beans can be frozen, either as a whole or divided into individual portions. Defrost thoroughly before reheating.

 Make ahead

You could make the Mexican chilli beans up to 2 days ahead of serving. Leave to cool, then store, covered, in the fridge. Reheat for 5–7 minutes before serving.

Noodles with Sichuan peanut sauce

Sichuan cooking is known for being chilli-hot and if you like it spicy, this quick stir-fry won't disappoint. But if chilli really isn't your thing, you can leave it out without spoiling the dish.

Serves 4

25 minutes in total

7 ProPoints values per serving

27 ProPoints values per recipe

40 g (1½ oz) reduced fat peanut butter

4 tablespoons light coconut milk

300 ml (10 fl oz) hot vegetable stock

2 tablespoons soy sauce

1 teaspoon toasted sesame oil

200 g (7 oz) dried brown rice vermicelli noodles

125 g (4½ oz) small **broccoli** florets

calorie controlled cooking spray

1 large red **pepper**, de-seeded and sliced thinly

125 g (4½ oz) **sugar snap peas** or **mange tout**, halved

4 **spring onions**, sliced thinly

3 **garlic cloves**, chopped

2.5 cm (1 inch) **fresh root ginger**, peeled and grated

1 tablespoon mild curry powder

½–1 teaspoon chilli flakes, or to taste (optional)

1 Stir the peanut butter and coconut milk into the hot stock until combined, then add the soy sauce and sesame oil.

2 Bring a large saucepan of water to the boil and cook the noodles according to the packet instructions. Add the broccoli florets 3 minutes before the end of the noodle cooking time. Drain the noodles and broccoli in a colander and place under cold running water until cold.

3 Heat a wok or large non stick frying pan over a medium-high heat. Spray with the cooking spray and stir-fry the red pepper, sugar snap peas or mange tout, spring onions, garlic, ginger, curry powder and chilli flakes, if using, for 2 minutes.

4 Add the noodles and broccoli to the wok, then pour in the peanut sauce. Toss everything together and warm through for a couple of minutes, then serve in bowls.

 Try this

If you have any leftover chicken from the Sunday roast, why not add it to this stir-fry for a non vegetarian option? For four people, stir in 200 g (7 oz) cooked **shredded skinless chicken** with the noodles and broccoli in Step 4 and heat through for an extra 2 **ProPoints** values per serving.

Hungry family hint

This ideal family supper can be served with a 120 g pack of Quorn satay skewers for four, for an extra 6 **ProPoints** values per serving.

Hoisin tofu

Serve this terrific oriental tofu dish with steamed **sugar snap peas** and **broccoli** and 50 g (1¾ oz) dried jasmine rice per person, cooked according to packet instructions, for an extra 5 **ProPoints** values per serving.

Serves 4
20 minutes in total
5 ProPoints values per serving
19 ProPoints values per recipe

1 teaspoon toasted sesame oil

2.5 cm (1 inch) **fresh root ginger**, peeled and chopped finely

100 ml (3½ fl oz) dry sherry or Chinese rice wine

1 star anise

2 tablespoons soy sauce

3 tablespoons hoisin sauce

400 g (14 oz) firm **tofu**, drained and patted dry, cut in half horizontally then sliced into 12 x 1 cm (½ inch) thick slices

2 **spring onions**, sliced thinly diagonally, to garnish

1 Heat a wok or large non stick frying pan over a medium heat. Add the sesame oil to the wok and stir-fry the ginger for 30 seconds. Add the dry sherry and star anise and cook for 2 minutes or until the liquid has reduced by half, then stir in the soy sauce, hoisin sauce and 4 tablespoons of water. Add the tofu and spoon the sauce over the top.

2 Reduce the heat to low and simmer for 5 minutes, occasionally spooning the sauce over the tofu. Using a spatula or slotted spoon, remove the tofu from the wok and set aside. Increase the heat to medium and cook the sauce for 2 minutes until reduced and thickened.

3 Remove the star anise. Divide the tofu between four shallow bowls and spoon the sauce over the top. Sprinkle with the spring onions before serving.

Pesto soufflé omelette

Enjoy with a 40 g (1½ oz) slice of crusty bread per person and a **tomato** and **rocket** salad for an extra 2 **ProPoints** values per serving.

Serves 2
15 minutes in total
3 ProPoints values per serving
6 ProPoints values per recipe

2 **eggs**, separated

1 teaspoon low fat spread

calorie controlled cooking spray

2 teaspoons reduced fat pesto

a small handful of **fresh basil** leaves

salt and freshly ground black pepper

1 Whisk the egg whites using an electric hand whisk for about 2 minutes until they form stiff peaks. Lightly beat the egg yolks in a separate bowl, season and fold them into the egg whites using a metal spoon or spatula.

2 Melt the spread in a large, non stick frying pan. Tilt the pan until the base is coated, then spray all over with the cooking spray.

3 Briefly remove the pan from the heat, add the egg mixture and spread it out in an even layer. Return to the heat and cook for 2 minutes until the base is set and starting to turn golden. Spoon the pesto down the centre, season with black pepper and scatter over the basil leaves.

4 Fold the omelette in half and cook for another 1–2 minutes until the centre is heated through. Cut the omelette in half and serve it straight away, garnished with more basil.

Fold the egg yolks into the egg whites.

Spread out the egg mixture in an even layer.

Fold the omelette in half. Cook for 1 or 2 minutes.

Here's an easy supper for when you need to rustle up something quickly.

Filo egg baskets with fresh tomato pickle

Serve these attractive tartlets with a crisp and delicious green **salad**, for no extra *ProPoints* values.

Serves 4

45 minutes in total

6 *ProPoints* values per serving

22 *ProPoints* values per recipe

2 x 45 g sheets Jus-Rol filo pastry,
  each measuring 50 x 24 cm
  (20 x 9½ inches), defrosted if frozen

4 **eggs**

3 tablespoons **skimmed milk**

250 g (9 oz) chestnut **mushrooms**,
  sliced

2 **garlic cloves**, chopped finely

salt and freshly ground black pepper

1 tablespoon finely chopped **fresh
  parsley**, to garnish (optional)

For the fresh tomato pickle

1 teaspoon olive oil

1 **onion**, chopped finely

calorie controlled cooking spray

3 large **tomatoes**, de-seeded and
  chopped

4 teaspoons white wine vinegar

2 teaspoons soft brown sugar

1 To make the fresh tomato pickle, heat the olive oil in a medium lidded saucepan and add the onion. Spray with the cooking spray and cook, covered, for 8 minutes, stirring occasionally, until softened. Add the tomatoes, vinegar and sugar, then season. Bring to the boil, then turn the heat down to low, part-cover the pan, and simmer for 10 minutes until the mixture has reduced and thickened. Set aside to cool while you make the filo baskets.

2 Preheat the oven to Gas Mark 6/200°C/fan oven180°C. Put one sheet of filo pastry on a work surface and cut into two, then cut each half into four equal squares and spray them with the cooking spray. Spray four holes of a deep muffin tin with the cooking spray. Stack four squares of filo pastry together, offset at angles, then gently press the stack into one of the holes to make a pastry case. Repeat with the remaining filo pastry sheets to make four pastry cases in total.

3 Beat the eggs and milk in a jug until combined, then season. Carefullly pour the mixture into the filo pastry cases and bake for 18–20 minutes until risen and set.

4 Meanwhile, heat a large, non stick frying pan, spray with the cooking spray and cook the mushrooms for 5 minutes until softened. Add the garlic and fry for another minute.

5 Serve the tarts with 1 tablespoon of the fresh tomato pickle, the garlic mushrooms and a sprinkling of parsley, if using.

 Leftovers tip

You can keep any leftover tomato pickle in an airtight jar in the fridge for up to 2 weeks. Alternatively, why not make it ahead and store it in the fridge until ready to use? The pickle is also great with sliced ham, cheese or sausages.

Cut each half of the pastry
into four squares.

Place the pastry stacks
in the muffin tray.

Pour the egg and milk
mixture into the cases.

Italian Quorn and mozzarella bake

A mandolin isn't an essential piece of kitchen equipment, but it certainly makes light work of slicing vegetables thinly. You can use a sharp knife if you don't have one. In this recipe, the potatoes are cut into thin slices and form a crisp, golden topping. Serve with steamed fine **green beans** for no extra *ProPoints* values.

Serves 4

Preparation time 40 minutes

Cooking time 40 minutes

7 *ProPoints* values per serving

29 *ProPoints* values per recipe

(V)

calorie controlled cooking spray

2 **onions**, chopped finely

1 **celery** stick, chopped finely

1 red **pepper**, de-seeded and diced

3 **garlic cloves**, chopped

2 teaspoons dried Italian herbs

350 g (12 oz) **Quorn mince**

400 g can chopped **tomatoes**

1 tablespoon tomato ketchup

1 red **chilli**, de-seeded and chopped (optional)

200 ml (7 fl oz) white wine

300 g (10½ oz) **potatoes**, unpeeled and sliced very thinly into rounds

150 g (5½ oz) light mozzarella, drained, patted dry and sliced

salt and freshly ground black pepper

1 Heat a large lidded saucepan and spray with the cooking spray. Cook the onion for 8 minutes, covered, until softened. Stir the onions occasionally. Add the celery, red pepper, garlic and herbs and cook for another 5 minutes until the vegetables have softened.

2 Add the Quorn mince with the canned tomatoes, ketchup, chilli, if using, and white wine and stir thoroughly. Bring to the boil, then reduce the heat and simmer, part-covered, for 10 minutes, until the sauce has reduced and thickened. Season well.

3 Meanwhile, preheat the oven to Gas Mark 6/200°C/fan oven 180°C. Put the potatoes in a large saucepan, cover with water and bring to the boil. Cook the potatoes for 8 minutes until tender – they should be soft but not falling apart. Drain and rinse under cold running water, then drain again.

4 Spoon the Quorn mixture into a 23 x 29 cm (9 x 11½ inch) ovenproof dish. Arrange the slices of potato on top and scatter with the mozzarella. Spray the top with the cooking spray and bake in the oven for 30–40 minutes, until golden.

 Try this

Why not serve the Quorn sauce on top of pasta instead? Omit the potatoes and prepare the sauce following the instructions above. Cook 200 g (7 oz) dried spaghetti according to the packet instructions for 10 minutes until al dente, then serve with the sauce. The *ProPoints* values will be 10 per serving.

Sausage and aubergine hot pot with polenta

This hot pot has a rich, lightly spiced tomato sauce and is served with the ready-made polenta that can usually be found alongside the dried pasta or rice in supermarkets. You could also serve the hot pot with a 40 g (1½ oz) slice of ciabatta per person for an additional 3 **ProPoints** values per serving.

Serves 4

40 minutes in total

7 ProPoints values per serving

29 ProPoints values per recipe

 (excluding the polenta)

425 g (15 oz) **aubergine**, peeled and
  cut into small pieces

6 Quorn sausages

calorie controlled cooking spray

1 teaspoon olive oil

4 **garlic cloves**, chopped finely

500 g (1 lb 2 oz) **passata**

1 teaspoon tomato purée

1 teaspoon dried thyme

1 teaspoon ground cumin

1 teaspoon ground coriander

a pinch of sugar

½ teaspoon chilli flakes (optional)

200 g (7 oz) ready-made polenta, cut
  into 8 x 1 cm (½ inch) thick slices

salt and freshly ground black pepper

a few **fresh coriander** leaves, to
  garnish

1 Cook the aubergine in a steamer, placed over a pan of simmering water, until very soft. This will take about 10–14 minutes. Transfer the aubergine to a bowl and mash with the back of a fork to make a coarse purée.

2 Meanwhile, preheat the grill to high and line the grill pan with foil. Spray the sausages with the cooking spray and grill for 8 minutes, turning occasionally, until browned. Remove from the grill and cut into 1 cm (½ inch) slices.

3 Put the olive oil and garlic in a medium lidded saucepan and fry for 30 seconds over a medium heat, stirring occasionally, until softened. Try not to let the garlic brown. Spray with the cooking spray and add the passata, tomato purée, thyme, cumin, coriander, sugar and chilli flakes, if using. Cook for 5 minutes, part-covered, stirring occasionally.

4 Add the steamed aubergine, stir well and part-cover. Simmer for another 8 minutes until the sauce has reduced and thickened. Season, then add the cooked sausage and heat through for 2 minutes.

5 While the stew is cooking, heat a griddle pan or large, non stick frying pan. Spray the polenta slices with the cooking spray and griddle for 5–6 minutes, turning once, until golden in places. Serve the hot pot topped with the polenta and sprinkled with some coriander.

 Ingredient tip

There's nothing like the taste of fresh herbs to lift a dish. To keep them in peak condition, wrap the stalks in a damp sheet of kitchen towel and put in a loose plastic bag. They should then keep for up to 1 week in the fridge. Alternatively, chop the herbs and freeze them in a little water in ice cube trays – they will keep for up to 1 month.

Winter chestnut stew with sweet potato mash

Chestnuts, porcini mushrooms, shallots and thyme come together to make a wonderfully warming, filling stew, which is served with a garlicky sweet potato mash.

Serves 4

40 minutes in total + soaking

7 *ProPoints* values per serving

27 *ProPoints* values per recipe

 (stew only)

15 g (½ oz) dried porcini mushrooms

½ a kettleful of boiling water

calorie controlled cooking spray

500 g (1 lb 2 oz) **shallots**, peeled and halved, if large

250 g (9 oz) **mushrooms**, halved, if large

3 **garlic cloves**, 2 chopped and 1 halved

2 teaspoons dried thyme

100 ml (3½ fl oz) dry sherry

200 g (7 oz) cooked chestnuts (vacuum packed or tinned), halved

1 tablespoon soy sauce

450 g (1 lb) **sweet potatoes**, peeled and cubed

1 heaped teaspoon cornflour

salt and freshly ground black pepper

a few **fresh thyme** sprigs, to garnish (optional)

1 Soak the porcini mushrooms in 300 ml (10 fl oz) boiling hot water for 20 minutes until softened. Strain the porcini mushrooms, reserving the soaking liquid.

2 Heat a large, lidded casserole pan over a medium heat and spray with the cooking spray. Cook the shallots, covered, for 10 minutes until softened, stirring occasionally. Add the soaked porcini and mushrooms, chopped garlic and thyme, spray with extra cooking spray, and cook for 5 minutes, until softened.

3 Pour in the sherry and allow it to bubble away for 2 minutes until it has reduced by a third and there is no smell of alcohol. Pour in the reserved porcini soaking liquid, then add the chestnuts and soy sauce. Bring to the boil, then reduce the heat to low, cover and simmer for 12 minutes.

4 Meanwhile, put the sweet potatoes in a medium size lidded pan and cover with cold water. Add the halved garlic clove and bring to the boil. Reduce the heat slightly, part-cover and simmer for 10 minutes or until tender. Drain the sweet potatoes and garlic, return them to the pan and mash until smooth.

5 Mix the cornflour into a little cold water and add to the stew. Stir for 3 minutes until the sauce has thickened and the vegetables are tender, then season.

6 Serve the stew on plates, garnished with the thyme sprigs, if using, and with the sweet potato mash by the side.

Hungry family hint

Enjoy mopping up the tasty juices from the stew with a 40 g (1½ oz) slice of ciabatta bread per person for an additional 3 ***ProPoints*** values per serving.

Short cut
suppers

After a busy day, turn to this *wonderful* selection of quick and easy suppers to find something *fast* to cook that your *family* will enjoy and will also keep you within your *ProPoints* allowance.

Mexican bean and tomato soup

Fajita spices add a superb flavour to this chunky soup. Finish with a swirl of cooling soured cream and crunchy tortilla chips.

Serves 4
Preparation time 10 minutes
Cooking time 25 minutes
3 ProPoints values per serving
13 ProPoints values per recipe
 (soup only)

calorie controlled cooking spray
400 g (14 oz) prepared zero **ProPoints**
  value chopped vegetables for soup,
  including **onion, carrot** and **celery**
400 g (14 oz) can **mixed beans in**
  water, drained and rinsed
500 ml (18 fl oz) **passata with garlic**
  and herbs
500 ml (18 fl oz) vegetable stock
2 teaspoons fajita spice mix
4 teaspoons reduced fat soured cream
18 g pack Weight Watchers Nacho
  Cheese Tortillas
salt and freshly ground black pepper

1 Spray a large lidded saucepan with the cooking spray and sauté the prepared vegetables for 5 minutes over a medium heat, stirring occasionally. Add the mixed beans, passata, stock and fajita spice mix.

2 Bring to the boil, then reduce the heat, part-cover, and simmer for 20–25 minutes, until the vegetables are tender and the soup has reduced and thickened. Season.

3 Ladle the soup into bowls and top with a spoonful of the soured cream. Scatter the nachos over the top.

 Make ahead

This filling soup will keep for up to 3 days if stored in the fridge. Reheat thoroughly before serving, then top with the soured cream and tortillas. You can also freeze the soup for up to 1 month.

Hungry family hint

Stir a chopped Mexican- or Cajun-style cooked mini chicken breast (145 g/5¼ oz) into each serving of soup for an extra 5 **ProPoints** values per serving.

Ratatouille with bruschetta

This meat-free dish ticks all the right boxes when it comes to ease, simplicity and flavour.

Serves 2
15 minutes in total
12 *ProPoints* values per serving
25 *ProPoints* values per recipe

2 medium slices country-style bread
1 **garlic clove**, halved
390 g can ratatouille
50 g (1¾ oz) stoned black olives in brine, drained
1 teaspoon dried oregano
freshly ground black pepper
a few **fresh basil** leaves, torn, to garnish (optional)

1 Heat a ridged griddle pan over a high heat for a few minutes. Put the bread on the griddle and toast for 5 minutes, turning once and pressing the bread down with a spatula. Remove from the griddle and rub one half of the garlic over each slice.

2 Meanwhile, heat the ratatouille, olives and oregano in a medium saucepan over a medium-low heat until warmed through, stirring occasionally. Do not allow the mixture to boil.

3 Put a slice of toast on each serving plate. Spoon the ratatouille on top, season with black pepper and scatter over the basil, if using.

Veg mac 'n' cheese

Serves 4
20 minutes in total
6 *ProPoints* values per serving
25 *ProPoints* values per recipe

200 g (7 oz) fresh penne pasta
150 g (5½ oz) small **cauliflower** florets
150 g (5½ oz) small **broccoli** florets
40 g packet Cheddar cheese sauce mix
400 ml (14 fl oz) semi skimmed milk
1 teaspoon wholegrain mustard
2 **tomatoes**, sliced into rounds
freshly ground black pepper

1 Bring a large saucepan of water to the boil and cook the pasta, cauliflower and broccoli for 5–6 minutes until the pasta is cooked and the vegetables are tender, then drain.

2 Meanwhile, preheat the grill to medium high. Empty the sachet of Cheddar cheese sauce mix into a small saucepan and whisk in a little of the milk. Stir in the remaining milk and bring to the boil, stirring continuously. Reduce the heat and simmer for 2 minutes until thickened, then stir in the mustard and season with black pepper, to taste.

3 Transfer the pasta and vegetables to a medium size ovenproof dish, pour the sauce over the top and stir until combined. Top with the tomatoes, and grill for 5 minutes, until the top begins to brown.

 Freezing tip
This recipe freezes well as a finished dish, or in individual portions. Leave it to cool, transfer to a lidded freezerproof container, and freeze for up to 1 month.

Who says you can't cook for the family and be on a diet?

Stuffed portobello mushrooms

Serve these tasty stuffed mushrooms with steamed or boiled Savoy **cabbage** and **leeks** for no extra *ProPoints* values.

Serves 4

Preparation time 15 minutes

Cooking time 25 minutes

5 *ProPoints* values per serving

19 *ProPoints* values per recipe

100 g (3½ oz) packet wild mushroom flavoured couscous

75 g (2¾ oz) **lean wafer thin smoked ham**, cut into small pieces

4 large portobello **mushrooms**, stalks removed and discarded

calorie controlled cooking spray

125 g (4½ oz) light mozzarella, cut into 4 slices

freshly ground black pepper

1 Preheat the oven to Gas Mark 5/190°C/fan oven 170°C. Prepare the couscous according to the packet instructions. When the couscous has absorbed the water, stir in the ham and season with black pepper.

2 Spray both sides of the mushrooms with the cooking spray and put, cap-side down, on a baking tray. Divide the couscous mixture between the mushrooms, spooning it on top in piles, and press it down slightly. Spray the top of the couscous with the cooking spray and top with the mozzarella. Bake for 20–25 minutes until the mushrooms have softened and the mozzarella has melted.

 Try this

You can try other varieties of flavoured couscous to make the stuffing – Moroccan spiced couscous also works well.

More to spend?

Why not try adding 100 g (3½ oz) new **potatoes** per person, for an extra 2 *ProPoints* values per serving, or enjoy a 125 ml (4 fl oz) glass of chilled dry white wine for an extra 3 *ProPoints* values per serving?

Hot beef salad

Thai red curry paste is not only great for curries and soups but also makes a zingy extra in salads.

Serves 2

15 minutes in total

7 *ProPoints* values per serving

14 *ProPoints* values per recipe

225 g (8 oz) medallion steak, cut into thin strips

1 tablespoon Thai red curry paste

60 g (2 oz) **watercress**, **rocket** and **spinach** salad

1 red **pepper**, de-seeded and sliced

2 **spring onions**, sliced

40 g (1½ oz) **sugar snap peas**

calorie controlled cooking spray

salt and freshly ground black pepper

For the dressing

juice of a lime

1 teaspoon clear honey

1 Put the beef in a bowl and add half the red curry paste. Season and stir until combined. (The beef can be cooked immediately or left to marinate for up to 1 hour.)

2 Divide the salad leaves, red pepper, spring onions and sugar snap peas between two plates and set aside.

3 To make the dressing, mix together the remaining red curry paste, lime juice and honey with 1 tablespoon of warm water. Season the dressing, then drizzle it over the salad.

4 Heat a wok or large frying pan over a high heat. Spray the beef with the cooking spray and add to the wok. Spread the beef out in the wok and cook for 1 minute until browned, then stir-fry for 2 minutes until cooked through. Remove from the heat and spoon the beef over the salad. Serve immediately.

 Try this

You can make this salad with 225 g (8 oz) **pork loin steak**, sliced thinly, instead of the beef, for the same ***ProPoints*** values per serving. Prepare the pork as described for the beef, then stir-fry it for 5 minutes, following the instructions in Step 4, until cooked through.

 Make ahead

The dressing will keep, stored in an airtight container in the fridge, for up to 1 week.

Spanish chorizo one-pot

This Spanish-style stew is delicious served on top of a 225 g (8 oz) **potato**, baked in its skin, per person, for an extra 5 **ProPoints** values per serving. Don't worry if you can't find smoked paprika. You can use regular paprika and add half a chopped and de-seeded medium-hot red **chilli** instead.

Serves 4

25 minutes in total

4 ProPoints values per serving

17 ProPoints values per recipe

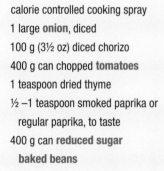

calorie controlled cooking spray

1 large **onion**, diced

100 g (3½ oz) diced chorizo

400 g can chopped **tomatoes**

1 teaspoon dried thyme

½ –1 teaspoon smoked paprika or
    regular paprika, to taste

400 g can **reduced sugar**
    baked beans

1 Heat a large lidded saucepan over a medium heat. Spray with the cooking spray, add the onion and fry for 5 minutes, covered, until softened. Stir the onions occasionally. Add the chorizo and cook, uncovered, for another 3 minutes, until it starts to crisp.

2 Add the chopped tomatoes, thyme and smoked paprika and bring to the boil, then turn the heat down slightly and simmer, part-covered, for 8 minutes. Add the baked beans and cook for another 3 minutes until reduced and thickened. Serve straight away.

V Veggie swap

For a vegetarian version, replace the chorizo with a 125 g pack of **Quorn Deli Bacon Style Rashers**. Cut into pieces and add to the pan in place of the chorizo in Step 1. Cook for 2 minutes, stirring occasionally, for a **ProPoints** value of 3 per serving.

Hungry family hint

This is extra filling with sausages. You can add any sausage but you might like to try two grilled Weight Watchers premium pork sausages per person for an extra 2 **ProPoints** values per serving.

Sausages with white bean 'mash' and red onion relish

This meal is also fantastic with **kale** and **broccoli** for no extra *ProPoints* values, or with 80 g (3 oz) **peas** per person for an extra 2 *ProPoints* values per serving.

Serves 4

25 minutes in total

7 *ProPoints* values per serving

28 *ProPoints* values per recipe

450 g pack half fat sausages

2 x 400 g cans **butter beans in water**, drained and rinsed

2 large **garlic cloves**, crushed

calorie controlled cooking spray

1 teaspoon dried mixed Italian herbs

200 ml (7 fl oz) vegetable stock

For the red onion relish

1 red **onion**, sliced thinly

2 teaspoons red wine vinegar or balsamic vinegar

½ teaspoon sugar

freshly ground black pepper

1 Preheat the grill to medium and line the grill pan with foil. Grill the sausages, turning them occasionally, for 16–18 minutes or until cooked and browned all over.

2 While the sausages are cooking, put the beans in a saucepan with the garlic over a medium heat. Spray with the cooking spray and cook for 30 seconds, stirring continuously. Add the herbs and stock and bring to the boil, then reduce the heat and simmer for 3 minutes until the beans have softened.

3 To make the red onion relish, put the onion in a saucepan with the vinegar and 2 tablespoons of cold water. Heat over a medium heat and simmer for 2–3 minutes until soft. Add the sugar, then season with black pepper.

4 Mash the beans with a potato masher until they make a rough purée – or you could blend them in a blender or food processor. Season with black pepper and serve the sausages with the bean 'mash' and the red onion relish, spooning over any juices from the pan.

Veggie swap

Vegetarian sausages would also taste good with this bean mash, instead of the regular variety. Look for the Cumberland-style ones and grill two sausages per person for 15 minutes or until browned all over for 6 *ProPoints* values per serving.

For any fussy eaters in the family, go ahead and serve with mashed potatoes on the side instead of mashed beans.

Flash-fried sweet chilli and garlic prawns

This satisfying, quick and vibrant prawn dish is just the thing after a day at work. It's lovely with steamed broccoli florets for no extra *ProPoints* values.

Serves 4

10 minutes in total

5 *ProPoints* values per serving

19 *ProPoints* values per recipe

calorie controlled cooking spray

5 cm (2 inches) **fresh root ginger**, peeled and cut into fine matchsticks or 2 teaspoons ginger paste

250 g (9 oz) raw peeled **prawns**

400 g can cherry **tomatoes**, drained

120 g sachet Blue Dragon sweet chilli and garlic stir-fry sauce

juice of ½ a lime

2 **spring onions**, sliced thinly

250 g pack Uncle Ben's Express basmati rice

1 Heat a wok or large, non stick frying pan over a high heat and spray with the cooking spray. Add the ginger and stir-fry for 30 seconds, then add the prawns and stir-fry for 2 minutes until pink all over.

2 Add the cherry tomatoes and sweet chilli and garlic stir-fry sauce and heat through, stirring, for 1–2 minutes. Add the lime juice and scatter the spring onions over the top.

3 Meanwhile, prepare the rice according to the packet instructions. Serve the stir-fry on top of the rice.

If you had the take away alternative, you would need to spend a lot more of your *ProPoints* allowance.

Hot-smoked trout with beetroot relish

Serve the trout and relish with 100 g (3½ oz) boiled new **potatoes** and a large handful of **watercress** per person for an extra 2 **ProPoints** values per serving.

Serves 2

10 minutes in total

3 ProPoints values per serving

5 ProPoints values per recipe

2 x 65 g (2¼ oz) cooked **hot-smoked trout fillets**

For the beetroot relish

150 g (5½ oz) cooked **beetroot**, diced

2 tablespoons **virtually fat free plain yogurt**

2 teaspoons lemon juice

1 **garlic clove**, crushed

½ teaspoon cumin seeds

salt and freshly ground black pepper

1 To make the beetroot relish, mix together the beetroot, yogurt, lemon juice and garlic in a bowl. (You can also purée the beetroot mixture using a hand blender, if you prefer a smooth relish.) Season the relish.

2 Put a smoked trout fillet on each serving plate, or flake it into pieces, and serve with the beetroot relish. Sprinkle the cumin seeds over the top.

 *Try this*

The same amount of smoked salmon would make a delicious alternative to the hot-smoked trout, for the same **ProPoints** values per serving.

 *Make ahead*

The beetroot relish will keep in the fridge for up to 3 days. Sprinkle the cumin seeds over just before serving.

Tuna and egg fried rice

A great family dish that makes good use of everyday ingredients.

Serves 4
10 minutes in total
8 *ProPoints* values per serving
32 *ProPoints* values per recipe

calorie controlled cooking spray
4 cm (1½ inches) **fresh root ginger**, peeled and chopped finely
200 g (7 oz) frozen **petit pois**
2 x 250 g packs Uncle Ben's Express basmati rice
200 g (7 oz) can **tuna steak in spring water**, drained
2 **eggs**
2 tablespoons soy sauce
freshly ground black pepper

1 Heat a wok or large, non stick frying pan over a high heat. Spray with the cooking spray and add the ginger and petit pois. Stir-fry for 2 minutes until heated through. Add the rice, break it up with a fork, and stir-fry for 1 minute.
2 Add the tuna, and toss everything together until combined, then cook for 1 more minute. Turn the heat down to medium, crack the eggs into the wok, leave for a minute to allow them to cook slightly, then fold the eggs into the rice until they are cooked through.
3 Remove from the heat and stir in the soy sauce. Season and serve.

Hungry family hint
You could add 100 g (3½ oz) cooked peeled **prawns** to the rice with the tuna in Step 2 and heat through for an extra 2 ***ProPoints*** values per serving.

Pork and plum stir-fry

Nothing beats a stir-fry for speed and simplicity. This delicious pork stir-fry is no exception with its slightly sweet, glossy sauce.

Serves 4
10 minutes in total
9 *ProPoints* values per serving
34 *ProPoints* values per recipe

350 g (12 oz) **lean pork loin steak**, cut into thin strips
calorie controlled cooking spray
525 g pack prepared stir-fry mixed **vegetables**
3 tablespoons plum sauce
juice of a lime
2 tablespoons soy sauce
300 g (10½ oz) straight-to-wok medium egg noodles
freshly ground black pepper

1 Heat a wok or large non stick frying pan over a high heat. Add the pork, spray with the cooking spray, and stir-fry for 3 minutes until cooked through. Remove the pork and any juices from the wok and set to one side.
2 Add the stir-fry vegetables to the wok, spray again with the cooking spray, and stir-fry for 3 minutes.
3 Return the pork to the wok with the plum sauce, lime juice, soy sauce, 1 tablespoon of water and the noodles. Season with black pepper and stir-fry for 2 minutes, separating the noodles with a wok stirrer or spatula, until heated through. Serve immediately.

Turkey and spinach pasta bake

A dish that's certain to become a family favourite and simply needs side vegetables, such as **broccoli** and **carrots**, to make a complete meal, for no extra *ProPoints* values.

Serves 4

Preparation time 15 minutes

Cooking time 25 minutes

9 *ProPoints* values per serving

35 *ProPoints* values per recipe

calorie controlled cooking spray

500 g (1 lb 2 oz) **stir-fry turkey strips**

175 g (6 oz) baby **spinach** leaves

225 g (8 oz) fresh fusilli or penne pasta

1 teaspoon dried thyme

295 g can reduced fat condensed chicken soup

125 ml (4 fl oz) **skimmed milk**

salt and freshly ground black pepper

1 Preheat the oven to Gas Mark 4/180°C/fan oven 160°C. Heat a wok or large non stick frying pan over a medium-high heat. Spray with the cooking spray and stir-fry the turkey for 6 minutes, until browned all over.

2 Remove the turkey and set to one side, then add the spinach to the pan. Spray with more cooking spray and add a splash of water, then stir-fry the spinach for 1 minute, until just beginning to wilt.

3 Put the turkey, spinach, fresh pasta and thyme in a 30 x 24 cm (12 x 9½ inch) ovenproof dish and mix together. Pour the soup into a large jug. Pour the milk into the empty can and top up with enough water to fill the can, then stir this into the soup. Pour the diluted soup over the turkey mixture, season and stir until combined.

4 Cover the dish tightly with a lid or foil and bake for 15 minutes, then remove the lid or foil, spray with the cooking spray and cook for another 10 minutes until the top begins to turn golden. Serve immediately.

 *Ingredient tip*

If you can't find reduced fat condensed chicken soup, use the regular variety instead. The *ProPoints* values will be 10 per serving.

Chicken pitta pizzas

Put some **vegetable** crudités and a large green **salad** on the side for no extra **ProPoints** values per serving, or see the hint below.

Serves 4

10 minutes in total

7 ProPoints values per serving

30 ProPoints values per recipe

4 tablespoons **passata with garlic and herbs**

4 wholemeal pitta breads

125 g (4½ oz) cooked **skinless chicken breast**, sliced

½ yellow or red **pepper**, de-seeded and sliced thinly

125 g pack light mozzarella, drained, patted dry and torn into pieces

calorie controlled cooking spray

4 teaspoons reduced fat pesto

salt and freshly ground black pepper

fresh basil leaves, to garnish

1 Preheat the grill to medium high.

2 Spread 1 tablespoon of the passata over each pitta bread, leaving a narrow border around the edge. Divide the chicken between the pittas and top with the pepper and mozzarella. Season the pizzas, spray with the cooking spray, then grill for 3 minutes.

3 Place a teaspoon of pesto on top of each pizza, divided into three dollops, then return to the grill for an extra 2 minutes, until the mozzarella has melted and the pitta is crisp. Serve, scattered with the basil leaves.

 Veggie swap

You could scatter 15 g (½ oz) stoned black olives over each pizza in place of the chicken for the same **ProPoints** values per serving.

Hungry family hint

Kids would love these with a 100 g (3½ oz) serving of oven chips per person for an extra 5 **ProPoints** values per serving.

Chicken stew with gnocchi dumplings

8 ProPoints value

This light but filling stew couldn't be easier to prepare, and the gnocchi make a great cheat's alternative to dumplings.

Serves 4

15 minutes in total

8 *ProPoints* values per serving

34 *ProPoints* values per recipe

 (stew only)

600 ml (20 fl oz) chicken stock

300 g (12 oz) zero ***ProPoints*** value ready-prepared **vegetables**, including **broccoli**, **leeks**, and **carrots**

75 g (2¾ oz) frozen **petit pois**

2 teaspoons cornflour

400 g (14 oz) gnocchi

250 g (9 oz) cooked **skinless chicken breast**

4 heaped teaspoons reduced fat pesto

freshly ground black pepper

a few **fresh flat leaf parsley** leaves, to garnish

1 Put the chicken stock in a large, lidded sauté pan or saucepan and heat to boiling point over a high heat. Add the prepared vegetables, turn down the heat slightly, then cover and simmer for 4–5 minutes until they are almost tender. Add the petit pois and heat through for 1 minute.

2 Stir the cornflour into a little cold water. Add to the pan and stir carefully, without breaking up the vegetables. Cook for a further 2 minutes until the stock has thickened to a sauce-like consistency.

3 Meanwhile, bring a large saucepan of water to the boil and add the gnocchi. Cook for about 2 minutes or until they rise to the surface. Drain and add them to the stew with the cooked chicken. Stir until combined and heated through. Season and serve in large shallow bowls, topped with a spoonful of pesto and garnished with parsley.

Hungry family hint

A 50 g (1¾ oz) crusty roll per person will add 4 ***ProPoints*** values per serving.

More to spend?

15 g (½ oz) grated fresh Parmesan cheese per person, sprinkled over the stew just before serving, will add 2 ***ProPoints*** values per serving.

Weekday roast red pepper chicken with baby roasties

The roasted red pepper mezze keeps the chicken breasts lovely and moist and it's delicious with fine **green beans**, steamed, for no extra *ProPoints* values.

Serves 4

Preparation time 5 minutes

Cooking time 45 minutes

7 *ProPoints* values per serving

28 *ProPoints* values per recipe

calorie controlled cooking spray

450 g (1 lb) baby new **potatoes**

4 x 175 g (6 oz) **skinless boneless chicken breasts**

60 g (2 oz) roasted red pepper mezze from a jar

4 vines of cherry **tomatoes**

salt and freshly ground black pepper

1 Preheat the oven to Gas Mark 6/200°C/fan oven 180°C. Spray a large roasting tin with the cooking spray, add the new potatoes and spray again. Roast in the oven for 15 minutes.

2 Place the chicken in the roasting tin with the potatoes. Season, then spoon a tablespoon of the roasted red pepper mezze on top of each chicken breast and spread until the top is coated.

3 Put the tin in the oven and cook the chicken for 20 minutes. After this time, check the chicken to see if it is ready by piercing it with a skewer. If there is no trace of pink and the juices run clear, transfer the chicken to a warm plate and cover loosely with foil to keep warm. If the chicken is not quite ready, return it to the oven for an additional 5 minutes, and repeat if necessary.

4 Turn the potatoes and add the tomatoes. Spray with the cooking spray and return the tin to the oven, then cook for another 5 minutes until the potatoes are cooked through and the tomatoes are just tender. Serve straight away, with the chicken.

More to spend?

This is delicious with half an avocado per person, sliced and served with a drizzle of balsamic vinegar, for an extra 4 *ProPoints* values per serving.

Mint and lemon lamb couscous

This meal-in-one can be rustled up in a matter of minutes.

Serves 4
15 minutes in total
11 *ProPoints* values per serving
44 *ProPoints* values per recipe

2 x 100 g packets lemon, mint and
   parsley flavoured couscous
150 g (5½ oz) frozen **petit pois**
400 g (14 oz) lean lamb leg steaks
calorie controlled cooking spray

To serve
4 tablespoons tzatziki
salt and freshly ground black pepper
a handful of **fresh mint** leaves (optional)

1 Prepare the couscous according to the packet instructions, covering it with a plate to keep it warm.
2 Meanwhile, add the petit pois to a medium saucepan of boiling water and simmer for 3–5 minutes, until tender. Drain and then stir them into the couscous.
3 Heat a griddle or large, non stick frying pan over a high heat. Spray both sides of the lamb steaks with the cooking spray and season. Griddle for 4 minutes, turning them every minute, until browned on the outside but still slightly pink in the centre. Cut the lamb into slices.
4 Divide the couscous between four plates, top with the sliced lamb and a spoonful of tzatziki. You could scatter over a few mint leaves, if you like.

 **Veggie swap**

As a vegetarian alternative, swap the lamb steaks for a 100 g (3½ oz) **Quorn Lamb Style Grill** per person for 10 **ProPoints** values per serving.

Lamb with tomato dahl

The simple, strong flavours of lamb and dahl will feel like a feast.

Serves 2
20 minutes in total
11 *ProPoints* values per serving
22 *ProPoints* values per recipe

150 g pack Ainsley Harriott lentil dahl
227 g can chopped **tomatoes**
2 x 125 g (4½ oz) lean lamb loin fillets
calorie controlled cooking spray
1 teaspoon ground coriander
salt and freshly ground black pepper

To serve
2 tablespoons **virtually fat free plain yogurt**
a few **fresh coriander** leaves (optional)

1 Make the lentil dahl according to the packet instructions, replacing 200 ml (7 fl oz) of the water with the chopped tomatoes.
2 While the dahl is cooking, spray both sides of each lamb fillet with the cooking spray, season, and sprinkle over the ground coriander.
3 Heat a griddle or non stick frying pan over a medium-high heat. Cook the lamb for about 3 minutes, turning once, or until cooked to your liking.
4 Spoon the dahl on to two plates, then top with the lamb and a spoonful of yogurt. Scatter with the fresh coriander, if you like.

Lamb fillet with pineapple salsa

Salsas are perfect for adding heaps of flavour to meat, poultry or fish. This fruity mint salsa is quick to make and goes particularly well with lamb. Serve with a warmed pitta bread and a **rocket** salad per person for an extra 4 **ProPoints** values per serving.

Serves 4

15 minutes in total

4 ProPoints values per serving

17 ProPoints values per recipe

500 g (1 lb 2 oz) lean lamb leg fillets, about 125 g (4½ oz) each

calorie controlled cooking spray

salt and freshly ground black pepper

For the pineapple salsa

435 g can crushed **pineapple in natural juice**, drained, with 2 tablespoons of the juice reserved

25 g (1 oz) pepperdew peppers or jalapeño **chillies** from a jar, drained and chopped roughly

juice of a lime

4 tablespoons chopped **fresh mint**

1 Mix together all the ingredients for the salsa and set to one side until ready to serve.

2 Heat a griddle or large non stick frying pan over a medium-high heat. Spray both sides of the lamb with the cooking spray and season. Cook the lamb for about 3 minutes, turning once, or until cooked to your liking.

3 Serve the lamb with the pineapple salsa.

 Try this

The pineapple salsa also goes particularly well with chicken. Grill a 175 g (6 oz) **skinless boneless chicken breast** per person instead of the lamb, for about 20 minutes, or until there is no sign of pink and it is cooked through. This will be the same **ProPoints** values per serving.

 Make ahead

You could make the salsa up to 2 hours ahead, if you like. This will also allow the flavours to mingle and blend together.

Minute steaks with quick tomato sauce

Enjoy your steak with a 40 g (1½ oz) slice of ciabatta bread for 3 **ProPoints** values per serving.

Serves 2

10 minutes in total

4 ProPoints values per serving

9 ProPoints values per recipe

❄ (tomato sauce only)

2 **garlic cloves**, chopped finely

calorie controlled cooking spray

400 g can cherry **tomatoes**, drained (see Leftovers tip)

½ teaspoon sugar

a handful of **fresh basil** leaves, torn, plus extra to garnish

2 minute steaks, about 125 g (4½ oz) each

salt and freshly ground black pepper

1 To make the sauce, put the garlic in a medium saucepan, spray with the cooking spray and fry over a medium heat for 30 seconds, stirring. Add the drained cherry tomatoes, sugar and basil. Season and simmer, stirring regularly, for 3 minutes, until reduced and slightly thickened.

2 Meanwhile, heat a griddle or large, non stick frying pan over a medium-high heat. Spray both sides of each steak with the cooking spray and season. Griddle the steaks for 1 minute on each side, or until cooked to your liking.

3 Serve the steaks accompanied by the tomato sauce. Garnish with basil.

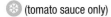 Leftovers tip

Don't throw away the drained tomato sauce from the cherry tomatoes; it can be used in a pasta sauce, soup or stew. It will keep in the fridge in an airtight container for up to 1 week or freeze it for up to 1 month.

Plan ahead to make sure you have added these ingredients to your shopping list, and then you'll have a quick and simple dinner in only 10 minutes.

Quick beef tacos

A fantastic family supper that's ready in only 15 minutes, but for an even quicker option, use **extra lean stir-fry beef** for the same *ProPoints* values per serving. Serve the tacos with sticks of **carrot, pepper, cucumber** and **celery** for no extra *ProPoints* values.

Serves 4

15 minutes in total

10 *ProPoints* values per serving

38 *ProPoints* values per recipe

calorie controlled cooking spray

300 g (10½ oz) **beef fillet**, sliced thinly

2 tablespoons fajita spice mix

220 g (7½ oz) prepared zero *ProPoints* value stir-fry **vegetable** medley

8 taco trays

60 g (2 oz) reduced fat guacamole

1 Preheat the oven to Gas Mark 4/180°C/fan oven 160°C.

2 Heat a wok or large non stick frying pan over a high heat. Spray with the cooking spray, turn the heat down slightly, and add the beef. Spread the beef out in the wok and leave for 1 minute until browned on the bottom, then stir-fry for another minute until cooked. Toss the beef in 1 teaspoon of the fajita spice mix. Using a slotted spoon or spatula, remove the beef from the wok, leaving any juices.

3 Spray the wok again and add the stir-fry vegetables. Stir-fry for 2 minutes, then return the beef to the wok with the remaining fajita spice mix and 2 tablespoons of water. Stir-fry for another 2 minutes.

4 Meanwhile, put the taco trays on a baking tray and place in the oven to warm through for 2–3 minutes.

5 Fill the taco trays with the beef stir-fry and put two on each serving plate. Top each one with a spoonful of the guacamole.

V *Veggie swap*

For a vegetarian version, swap the beef for 300 g (10½ oz) **Quorn Chicken Style Pieces** for 7 *ProPoints* values per serving.

Stir-fry the beef until browned and cooked.

Toss the beef and veg in the spice mix.

Fill the taco trays with the beef stir-fry.

The perfect alternative for a Friday night in. A restaurant version would set you back 19 *ProPoints* values.

Take aways
at home

No longer does a Friday night curry or a *Saturday pizza* need to blow your **ProPoints** budget. *Reclaim control* **of** *weekend* **nights with this delicious assortment of recipes that** *everyone* **will love.**

Oven baked fish

Enjoy delicious, home-made, golden and crispy beer batter, without a deep fat fryer in sight.

Serves 4
Preparation time 20 minutes
Cooking time 45 minutes
10 *ProPoints* values per serving
39 *ProPoints* values per recipe

500 g (1 lb 2 oz) **potatoes**, peeled and
   cut into 1 cm (½ inch) thick chips
calorie controlled cooking spray
4 x 150 g (5½ oz) skinless **cod loin
   fillets**
50 g (1¾ oz) low fat spread
100 g (3½ oz) plain flour
½ teaspoon bicarbonate of soda
1 **egg**, beaten
50 ml (2 fl oz) beer
salt and freshly ground black pepper

To serve
lemon wedges
fresh parsley sprigs

1 Preheat the oven to Gas Mark 7/220ºC/fan oven 200ºC. Arrange the chips in a single layer on a non stick baking tray. Spray with the cooking spray and bake in the oven on the top shelf for 25–30 minutes, turning halfway through the cooking time.

2 Meanwhile, arrange the cod fillets on another non stick baking tray. In a bowl, cream together the low fat spread, flour and bicarbonate of soda. Beat in the egg until smooth and then mix in the beer until a thick batter is formed. Season.

3 After 30 minutes put the chips onto the lowest shelf in the oven and continue to cook for another 10–15 minutes until the fish is ready or the chips are golden and crispy. Spread the batter in a thick layer over the top of each cod fillet, trying not to let it go on the sides. Bake the cod fillets in the oven on the top shelf for 10–15 minutes, until the batter is puffed up and golden. Serve immediately with the chips, lemon wedges and parsley sprigs on the side.

More to spend?

For the full experience, serve with 80 g (3 oz) cooked **peas** per person, blended in a food processor, or using a hand blender, until mushy, for an extra 2 ***ProPoints*** values per serving. Add some grilled **tomato** halves too. Then pour the remaining 250 ml (9 fl oz) from the beer bottle into a glass and enjoy for an extra 4 ***ProPoints*** values per serving.

Coriander fish with crispy ginger

Full of vibrant flavours thanks to the herbs, ginger and spices, this light fish dish is delicious served with **spinach** and 40 g (1½ oz) dried **brown basmati** or jasmine rice per person, cooked according to the packet instructions, for an extra 4 *ProPoints* values per serving.

Serves 2

25 minutes in total

6 *ProPoints* values per serving

11 *ProPoints* values per recipe

calorie controlled cooking spray

½ teaspoon vegetable oil

4 cm (1½ inches) **fresh root ginger**, peeled and cut into matchsticks

2 x 200 g (7 oz) thick **cod fillets**

2 large **garlic cloves**, crushed

1 teaspoon ground coriander

½ teaspoon turmeric

½ teaspoon ground cumin

4 tablespoons **low fat plain bio yogurt**

1 tablespoon lemon juice

2 tablespoons chopped **fresh coriander**

salt and freshly ground black pepper

1 Preheat the grill to high and line the grill pan with foil. Spray a non stick frying pan with the cooking spray and add the oil. Add the ginger and fry for 3–5 minutes, stirring occasionally, until light golden and crisp. Drain on kitchen towel and set to one side until ready to use.

2 Season the fish and grill for 8–10 minutes, turning once, until cooked.

3 While the fish is grilling, spray the frying pan that you fried the ginger in with the cooking spray. Fry the garlic for 30 seconds, then stir in the spices. Turn the heat to low, add 3 tablespoons of water, the yogurt and the lemon juice. Stir until combined and gently heat through for 2 minutes or until reduced and slightly thickened. Add half of the fresh coriander and season.

4 Place the fish on plates and pour any juices from the grilled fish into the yogurt sauce. Stir the sauce, then spoon it over the fish and scatter over the crispy ginger and the remaining coriander. Serve immediately.

Goan prawn curry

This south Indian curry is subtly spiced with a lovely creamy sauce which is delicious with chicken too.

Serves 4

35 minutes in total

4 *ProPoints* values per serving

17 *ProPoints* values per recipe

calorie controlled cooking spray

1 large **onion**, grated

4 cm (1½ inches) **fresh root ginger**, peeled and grated

3 large **garlic cloves**, chopped finely

1 green **chilli**, de-seeded and chopped finely

1 teaspoon turmeric

1 tablespoon mild curry powder

3 cardamom pods, split

2 **tomatoes**, de-seeded and chopped

150 ml (5 fl oz) reduced fat coconut milk

100 ml (3½ fl oz) fish stock

100 g (3½ oz) **sugar snap peas**

400 g (14 oz) frozen peeled king **prawns**, defrosted and patted dry with kitchen towel

juice of a lime

½ teaspoon sugar

salt and freshly ground black pepper

2 tablespoons chopped **fresh coriander**, to serve

1 Heat a lidded saucepan over a medium heat, spray with the cooking spray and add the onion. Stir, cover, and cook for 8 minutes until softened. Stir the onion occasionally.

2 Add the ginger, garlic and chilli to the pan and cook, stirring, for 1 more minute, then add the turmeric, curry powder, cardamom, tomatoes, coconut milk and stock. Bring to the boil, then reduce the heat and simmer, part-covered, for 8 minutes until reduced and starting to thicken.

3 Stir in the sugar snap peas, prawns and lime juice and cook for about 3–4 minutes until the prawns are pink and cooked through. Season and add the sugar then stir in half the coriander. Sprinkle over the rest of the coriander just before serving.

 Cook's tip

Leftover coconut milk can be frozen for future use. Pour it into an ice cube tray, then transfer to a freezer bag once frozen. The coconut milk can be used from frozen.

Hungry family hint

Serve with 150 g (5½ oz) straight-to-wok rice noodles per person, cooked, for an additional 5 ***ProPoints*** values per serving.

Sausage pizza

Children love meatballs and this quick pizza is really fun to make with them – it's also a favourite with the grown-ups.

Serves 4

Preparation time 30 minutes

Cooking time 15 minutes

8 *ProPoints* values per serving

31 *ProPoints* values per recipe

145 g pizza base mix

calorie controlled cooking spray

2 tablespoons plain flour, for dusting

175 ml (6 fl oz) **passata**

1 teaspoon dried oregano

1 tablespoon tomato purée

½ teaspoon dried chilli flakes (optional)

4 reduced fat pork sausages

150 g (5½ oz) light mozzarella cheese, drained and torn into pieces

salt and freshly ground black pepper

a small handful of **fresh basil** leaves, to garnish

1 Prepare the pizza base mix according to the packet instructions. Spray a 25 x 35 cm (10 x 14 inch) baking tray with the cooking spray and dust with a little of the flour. Roll out the pizza dough thinly on a lightly floured work surface to a 23 x 30 cm (9 x 12 inch) rectangle. Transfer to the baking tray and set aside to rest for 10 minutes.

2 Meanwhile, preheat the oven to Gas Mark 7/220°C/fan oven 200°C. Mix together the passata, oregano, tomato purée and chilli flakes, if using. Spoon the sauce over the base in a thin layer, leaving a 1 cm (½ inch) border around the edge.

3 Squeeze the sausage meat out of the skins and make it into 28 marble-size balls. Arrange them on the top of the pizza, followed by the mozzarella, and season. Spray the top of the pizza with the cooking spray.

4 Bake in the oven for about 12–15 minutes until the base is golden and crisp. Garnish with the basil leaves and cut into four. Serve immediately.

V *Veggie swap*

Swap the pork sausages for four vegetarian sausages, sliced thinly, for 7 ***ProPoints*** values per serving.

Forget the take away tonight and get cooking this with the kids.

Family friendly

Balsamic chicken pizza

A hearty, meaty pizza that's wonderful to tuck into. It will definitely hit the spot!

Serves 2
Preparation time 40 minutes
Cooking time 12 minutes
8 *ProPoints* values per serving
16 *ProPoints* values per recipe

calorie controlled cooking spray
1 small **onion**, chopped finely
400 g can cherry **tomatoes in natural juice**
100 g (3½ oz) yellow cherry **tomatoes**, halved (optional)
1 tablespoon chopped **fresh basil** leaves, plus extra leaves, to garnish
100 g (3½ oz) **skinless boneless chicken breast**, chopped into 1 cm (½ inch) pieces
2 tablespoons balsamic vinegar
23 cm (9 inch) ready-made thin and crispy pizza base
1 yellow **pepper**, de-seeded and sliced (optional)
75 g (2¾ oz) light mozzarella, drained and torn into pieces
salt and freshly ground black pepper

1 To make the topping, spray a medium saucepan with the cooking spray and place over a medium heat. Add the onion and cook for about 5–7 minutes until softened, adding a little water if necessary. Add both sorts of tomatoes and the chopped basil. Bring to the boil and simmer for 20–25 minutes until thickened. Season and set aside.

2 Meanwhile, preheat the oven to Gas Mark 7/220 °C/fan oven 200°C. Put the chicken pieces in a small bowl with 1 tablespoon of the balsamic vinegar and set aside for 10 minutes.

3 Spray a small non stick frying pan with the cooking spray and place over a high heat. Add the chicken and the vinegar marinade. Cook, stirring, for about 3–5 minutes until the chicken is cooked through and most of the vinegar has evaporated. Add the remaining vinegar. Stir to deglaze the pan. Allow the vinegar to reduce for 1–2 minutes until it just coats the chicken and then remove the pan from the heat.

4 Spray a non stick baking tray with the cooking spray and put the pizza base on it. Spread the pizza base with the tomato sauce. Scatter with the chicken pieces and pepper, if using. Drizzle with any reduced vinegar in the pan and top with the mozzarella. Bake for 10–12 minutes until the base is golden and the cheese is bubbling. Serve immediately, garnished with the basil leaves.

Chicken dhansak

Enjoy with a Weight Watchers mini naan bread per person for an extra 3 *ProPoints* values per serving. A 60 g (2 oz) portion of dried basmati rice per person, cooked according to the packet instructions, will add 6 *ProPoints* values per serving.

Serves 2
Preparation time 30 minutes
Cooking time 20 minutes
7 ProPoints values per serving
15 ProPoints values per recipe
❄

60 g (2 oz) split red **lentils**, rinsed
calorie controlled cooking spray
1 **onion**, chopped
2 large **garlic cloves**, chopped
½ medium-hot green **chilli**, de-seeded and chopped
2.5 cm (1 inch) **fresh root ginger**, peeled and chopped finely
400 g can chopped **tomatoes**
150 ml (5 fl oz) vegetable stock
1 tablespoon medium curry powder
½ teaspoon cumin seeds
2 teaspoons tamarind paste
300 g (10½ oz) **skinless boneless chicken breasts**, cut into large bite size pieces
salt and freshly ground black pepper
a few **fresh coriander** leaves, to serve

1 Put the lentils in a small saucepan and cover with cold water. Bring to the boil, then turn the heat down to low and simmer for 10 minutes until tender. Drain.

2 While the lentils are cooking, spray a large lidded pan with the cooking spray. Cook the onion, covered, for 8 minutes, until softened. Stir the onions occasionally to prevent them from sticking. Add the garlic, chilli and ginger, then add a splash of water, and cook for 1 more minute.

3 Pour in the chopped tomatoes and stock, then stir in the curry powder, cumin seeds, tamarind paste and chicken. Bring to the boil, then turn the heat down and simmer, covered, for 12–15 minutes or until the chicken is cooked.

4 Add the lentils and cook, uncovered, for 5 more minutes until reduced and thickened. Season. Sprinkle with the coriander leaves before serving.

And with a little planning, you can have most of these ingredients in your store cupboard, making it a quick and simple dinner to make.

Chicken jalfrezi

Jalfrezi curries are cooked quickly in a similar way to a stir-fry. The chicken needs to be cut into small, same-sized pieces so that it cooks quickly and evenly. Serve with 60 g (2 oz) dried basmati rice per person, cooked according to the packet instructions, for an extra 6 **ProPoints** values per serving. A 42 g (1 oz) chapatti (page 150) per person will add 2 **ProPoints** values per serving. Top with a tablespoon of creamy low fat natural yogurt per person for an extra 1 **ProPoints** value per serving.

Serves 4

40 minutes in total

4 ProPoints values per serving

16 ProPoints values per recipe

calorie controlled cooking spray

2 **onions**, chopped

1 red **pepper**, de-seeded and sliced

2 **garlic cloves**, crushed

5 cm (2 inches) **fresh root ginger**, grated (no need to peel)

600 g (1 lb 5 oz) **skinless boneless chicken breasts**, diced

1 green **pepper**, de-seeded and sliced

1 green **chilli**, de-seeded and sliced thinly into rounds

1 tablespoon medium curry powder

1 teaspoon cumin seeds

400 g (14 oz) **passata**

salt and freshly ground black pepper

1 Heat a lidded saucepan over a medium heat. Spray with the cooking spray and stir-fry the onions for 5 minutes. Add the red pepper, garlic and ginger, spray again with the cooking spray, and stir-fry for another 3 minutes until the vegetables have softened.

2 Using a hand-held blender, purée the onion mixture with 4 tablespoons of water until smooth, then remove the onion mixture from the pan and set to one side until ready to use.

3 Return the pan to the heat, spray with the cooking spray, and stir-fry the chicken for 5 minutes until browned in places. Add the green pepper and chilli, then stir-fry for another 2 minutes.

4 Return the onion mixture to the pan and add the curry powder, cumin seeds and passata. Stir, bring to the boil, then reduce the heat and simmer, part-covered, for 10 minutes, until the sauce has reduced and thickened and the chicken has cooked through. Season and serve.

Add the red pepper, garlic and ginger to the cooked onions.

Whizz the onion mixture with water until smooth.

Add the passata, stir and cook for 10 minutes.

Pork vindaloo

This tasty curry has all the flavours of a traditional vindaloo, but without being overwhelmingly hot and, as an added bonus, it's also much quicker to make.

Serves 2

20 minutes in total

7 *ProPoints* values per serving

14 *ProPoints* values per recipe

calorie controlled cooking spray

250 g (9 oz) **lean pork loin steak**, cut into thin strips

1 **onion**, sliced thinly

1 red **pepper**, de-seeded and sliced

3 **garlic cloves**, chopped

2.5 cm (1 inch) **fresh root ginger**, peeled and sliced very thinly

1 teaspoon cumin seeds

1 teaspoon ground coriander

½ teaspoon turmeric

2 teaspoons tomato ketchup

2 teaspoons white wine vinegar

4 tablespoons vegetable stock

¼–½ teaspoon dried chilli flakes

freshly ground black pepper

To serve

1 tablespoon roughly chopped **fresh coriander**

2 tablespoons **low fat natural yogurt**

1 Heat a wok or large, non stick frying pan over a high heat. Spray with the cooking spray and add the pork. Spread the pork out in the wok and cook for 2 minutes until starting to brown. Turn the pork and cook for another 2 minutes until cooked through. Transfer the pork and any liquid in the wok to a plate and set to one side.

2 Reduce the heat slightly, spray with more cooking spray and add the onion to the wok or pan. Stir-fry the onion for 1 minute, then add the red pepper, garlic and ginger and stir-fry for 1 more minute.

3 Add the cumin seeds, ground coriander, turmeric, tomato ketchup, vinegar, stock and chilli flakes, then return the pork to the wok. Stir-fry for another minute and season with black pepper. Sprinkle with the fresh coriander and serve with 1 tablespoon of yogurt per person.

More to spend?

A 40 g (1½ oz) serving of dried **brown basmati rice** per person, cooked according to the packet instructions, will be an extra 4 ***ProPoints*** values per serving.

Lemon and ginger chicken

This delicious dish features the lovely combination of fresh lemon juice, ginger and honey.

Serves 4
30 minutes in total
6 *ProPoints* values per serving
23 *ProPoints* values per recipe

3 tablespoons light soy sauce
4 teaspoons clear honey
grated zest and juice of a small lemon
2 teaspoons cornflour
40 g (1½ oz) cashew nuts
500 g (1 lb 2 oz) **skinless boneless chicken breasts,** cut into strips
calorie controlled cooking spray
1 **onion**, sliced
2.5 cm (1 inch) **fresh root ginger**, peeled and chopped finely
100 g (3½ oz) **baby corn**, halved lengthways
125 g (4½ oz) **sugar snap peas**

1 Mix together the soy sauce, honey, lemon zest, lemon juice and cornflour in a shallow dish.
2 Put the cashews in a dry wok or non stick frying pan and dry-fry over a medium heat, turning occasionally, for 3–4 minutes until light golden. Set aside.
3 Heat the wok or non stick frying pan until hot, spray the chicken with the cooking spray and stir-fry for 5–6 minutes until golden all over. Remove from the pan and transfer the chicken to the soy sauce mixture. Turn until coated.
4 Spray the pan with the cooking spray and stir-fry the onion for 3 minutes. Add the ginger, baby corn and sugar snap peas then cook for another 2 minutes.
5 Return the chicken to the pan with the soy mixture and stir-fry for 1–2 minutes until the sauce is reduced and thickened. Serve topped with the toasted cashews.

Chicken laksa

If you can't find tom yum paste, use 2 tablespoons of red Thai curry paste instead, for the same *ProPoints* values per serving.

Serves 4
Preparation time 30 minutes
Cooking time 20 minutes
11 *ProPoints* values per serving
44 *ProPoints* values per recipe

calorie controlled cooking spray
4 x 150 g (5½ oz) **skinless boneless chicken breasts,** cut into bite size pieces
1 **onion**, sliced finely
1 red **pepper**, de-seeded and sliced finely
2 tablespoons tom yum paste
450 ml (16 fl oz) chicken stock
400 ml can reduced fat coconut milk
125 g (4½ oz) **sugar snap peas**
100 g (3½ oz) dried wholewheat noodles
220 g can **bamboo shoots in water**, drained
½ x 25 g pack **fresh coriander**, leaves only
lime wedges, to serve

1 Heat a lidded, deep, non stick saucepan and spray with the coooking spray. Add the chicken pieces and cook for 5 minutes, stirring until brown. You may need to do this in batches. Remove and set aside.
2 Add the onion and pepper to the saucepan and cook for 3–4 minutes until softened but not coloured. Stir in the tom yum paste and cook for 1 minute. Return the chicken pieces to the pan and pour in the stock and coconut milk. Bring to the boil, cover and simmer for 20 minutes.
3 Add the sugar snap peas, noodles and bamboo shoots. Cook, uncovered, for 2–3 minutes until tender, stirring occasionally to break up the noodles. Serve immediately in bowls, topped with the coriander, with the lime wedges on the side.

Special pork chow mein

Look for the fresh noodles in the vegetable aisle at the supermarket, beside the packs of stir-fry veggies.

Serves 4

40 minutes in total

8 *ProPoints* values per serving

31 *ProPoints* values per recipe

400 g (14 oz) **lean pork tenderloin**

1 tablespoon tandoori spice mix

calorie controlled cooking spray

4 tablespoons dark soy sauce

2 tablespoons rice wine vinegar

2 teaspoons tomato purée

1 **garlic clove,** crushed

1 red **chilli**, de-seeded and sliced finely

120 g pack shiitake **mushrooms**, wiped and sliced

1 **carrot**, peeled and cut into thin matchsticks

2 small **pak choi**, leaves separated from the stalks and stalks sliced finely, then both reserved

400 g pack fresh cooked egg noodles

60 g (2 oz) **beansprouts**

1 Preheat the oven to Gas Mark 6/200°C/fan oven 180°C and put a baking tray in to heat. Coat the pork in the tandoori spice mix and spray with the cooking spray. Heat a non stick frying pan until hot and cook the pork for 5 minutes, turning so that each side is brown. Remove the baking tray from the oven, transfer the pork to the tray and cook in the oven for 10–15 minutes until cooked.

2 Meanwhile, after 10 minutes, mix together the soy sauce, vinegar and tomato purée in a small jug. Set aside. Heat a wok or non stick frying pan until hot and spray with the cooking spray. Stir-fry the garlic and chilli for 1 minute, then add the mushrooms, carrots and pak choi stalks and cook for 5 minutes. Take off the heat.

3 Remove the pork from the oven and cover loosely with foil to keep warm. Set aside. Put the pan or wok back on the heat and add the noodles, beansprouts and pak choi leaves. Stir-fry for 3 minutes. Pour in the soy sauce mixture and cook gently for 1 minute, stirring until coated and combined and heated through. Divide the noodles between warm bowls, then thinly slice the pork and place it on top of the noodles. Serve immediately.

Saag aloo

This popular Indian side dish goes really well with most curries in place of rice, but would also be a good accompaniment to a 200 g (7 oz) piece of grilled **white fish** or a 175 g (6 oz) **skinless boneless chicken breast**, grilled, per person. Either will be 8 **ProPoints** values per serving.

Serves 4
25 minutes in total
2 ProPoints values per serving
8 ProPoints values per recipe

calorie controlled cooking spray
1 small **onion**, diced
350 g (12 oz) **potatoes**, peeled and cubed
1 tablespoon mild curry powder
1 teaspoon ground coriander
100 g (3½ oz) baby **spinach** leaves
salt and freshly ground black pepper

1 Heat a medium lidded saucepan over a medium heat. Spray with the cooking spray and cook the onion, covered, for 5 minutes until softened.
2 Add the potatoes, spices and 200 ml (7 fl oz) water and bring to the boil, then reduce the heat, cover, and simmer for 8 minutes until the potatoes are tender.
3 Add the spinach in three batches, stirring between each addition, until combined. Season and cook for 2 minutes until the spinach is wilted, then serve.

Lamb shashlik

Serve these lightly spiced lamb skewers with a 42 g (1½ oz) wholemeal chapatti per person for an extra 3 **ProPoints** values per serving. A tablespoon of mango chutney per person is delicious with the shashlik, for an extra 1 **ProPoints** value per serving.

Serves 4
30 minutes in total + marinating
4 ProPoints values per serving
17 ProPoints values per recipe

100 g (3½ oz) **virtually fat free plain yogurt**
1 tablespoon medium curry powder
1 teaspoon turmeric
1 teaspoon ground coriander
1 medium **chilli**, de-seeded and chopped finely
300 g (10½ oz) lean lamb steaks, trimmed of visible fat and cut into 2.5 cm (1 inch) pieces
1 green **pepper**, de-seeded and cut into 2.5 cm (1 inch) pieces
1 red **pepper**, de-seeded and cut into 2.5 cm (1 inch) pieces
1 red **onion**, halved and cut into wedges, then separated into layers
salt and freshly ground black pepper

1 Mix together the yogurt, curry powder, turmeric, coriander and chilli and season. Add the lamb, then stir until everything is coated in the spicy yogurt. Leave to marinate for at least 1 hour or preferably overnight in the fridge.
2 Preheat the grill to its highest setting and line the grill pan with foil. Divide the lamb and vegetables between the eight skewers, threading them in contrasting layers, and finishing each skewer with a piece of pepper.
3 Grill the skewers for 3–4 minutes on each side until cooked and turning golden in places. Serve two skewers per person.

Beef rogan josh

Serve this lovely curry with 40 g (1½ oz) dried **brown basmati rice** per person, cooked according to the packet instructions, for an extra 4 **ProPoints** values per person.

Serves 4
Preparation time 25 minutes
Cooking time 1 hour
5 ProPoints values per serving
21 ProPoints values per recipe

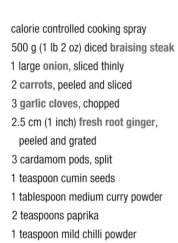

calorie controlled cooking spray
500 g (1 lb 2 oz) diced **braising steak**
1 large **onion**, sliced thinly
2 **carrots**, peeled and sliced
3 **garlic cloves**, chopped
2.5 cm (1 inch) **fresh root ginger**,
  peeled and grated
3 cardamom pods, split
1 teaspoon cumin seeds
1 tablespoon medium curry powder
2 teaspoons paprika
1 teaspoon mild chilli powder
2 tablespoons tomato purée
300 ml (10 fl oz) vegetable stock
salt and freshly ground black pepper

1 Heat a large, heavy based, lidded saucepan over a medium heat. Spray with the cooking spray and cook the beef for 6 minutes until browned all over. Remove the beef and any juices from the pan, then set to one side.

2 Add the onion and carrots to the pan and spray with more cooking spray, stir and cover. Cook the onion and carrots for 5 minutes over a medium heat until softened. Stir occasionally. Add the garlic, ginger, cardamom, cumin seeds, curry powder, paprika, chilli powder and tomato purée and stir to coat the vegetables in the spices.

3 Return the beef, and any juices, to the pan with the stock and bring to the boil, then reduce the heat to low and part-cover. Simmer gently, stirring occasionally, for 1 hour or until the beef is tender. Season before serving.

For when you want to put a bit of 'love' in your cooking, this is a great 'curry night' supper for the family.

Minced beef bhuna

Rice is the perfect accompaniment to this fragrant minced beef curry. Serve with 40 g (1½ oz) dried **brown basmati rice** per person, cooked according to the packet instructions, for an extra 4 **ProPoints** values per serving.

Serves 4
Preparation time 30 minutes
Cooking time 45 minutes
7 ProPoints values per serving
27 ProPoints values per recipe

calorie controlled cooking spray
500 g (1 lb 2 oz) extra lean beef mince
2 **onions**, sliced thinly
3 **garlic cloves**, chopped finely
5 cm (2 inches) **fresh root ginger**,
  grated (no need to peel)
1 red **pepper**, de-seeded and sliced
1 large **carrot**, peeled and diced
1½ tablespoons medium curry powder
2 teaspoons ground turmeric
2 tablespoons tamarind paste
4 tablespoons tomato purée
salt and freshly ground black pepper
fresh coriander sprigs, to garnish

1 Heat a large, heavy based, lidded saucepan over a medium heat. Spray with the cooking spray and add the mince. Cook for 5 minutes, breaking up the mince with a spatula, until the meat is browned all over.

2 Using a slotted spoon, remove the mince from the pan and set aside. Add the onions to the pan. Spray with more cooking spray and cook, covered, for 8 minutes until softened. Stir the onions occasionally.

3 Add the garlic, ginger, red pepper and carrot to the onions and cook for another minute, then add the spices, the tamarind paste and the tomato purée with 400 ml (14 fl oz) of water. Return the mince to the pan, and stir well to break up the tamarind paste, if necessary. When the curry starts to bubble, reduce the heat to low and cover. Simmer for 45 minutes, stirring occasionally, until the mince is tender and you have a rich, thick sauce. If the sauce is too thin, remove the lid and cook for another 5 minutes until it has thickened slightly. Season and serve, garnished with the coriander sprigs.

 Veggie swap

You could also make this curry using 350 g (12 oz) frozen **Quorn mince**, instead of the beef. Stir it into the pan in Step 3 at the same time as you would add the beef mince, but reduce the quantity of water to 300 ml (10 fl oz) and cook for 25 minutes from frozen. (There is no need to brown it first.) The **ProPoints** values will be 3 per serving.

 Ingredients tip

You could keep fresh root ginger in the freezer for up to 1 month. Store it in a sealed container and there's no need to defrost it before using – just grate it straight from frozen.

Spiced lentils with golden onions

Red split lentils don't need pre-soaking and cook more quickly than most lentils. One Weight Watchers mini naan bread per person is just the thing on the side, for an extra 3 *ProPoints* values per serving.

Serves 4

30 minutes in total

7 ProPoints values per serving

27 ProPoints values per recipe

225 g (8 oz) split red **lentils**, rinsed

2.5 cm (1 inch) **fresh root ginger**, peeled and cut into thin rounds

4 cardamom pods, split

calorie controlled cooking spray

2 **onions**, sliced thinly

3 **garlic cloves**, chopped finely

2 teaspoons cumin seeds

1 teaspoon turmeric

2 tablespoons medium curry paste

4 **tomatoes**, quartered, de-seeded and diced

salt and freshly ground black pepper

a small handful of **fresh coriander** leaves, to garnish

1 Put the lentils in a medium lidded saucepan with the ginger, cardamom and 1 litre (1¾ pints) of water. Bring to the boil, then reduce the heat, part-cover, and simmer for 15 minutes until very tender. Drain and remove the ginger and cardamom.

2 While the lentils are cooking, heat a second medium lidded non stick saucepan and spray with the cooking spray. Cook the onions, covered, for 10 minutes until softened. Stir the onions occasionally. Remove the lid and cook for another 5 minutes until the onions become light golden in colour. Add the garlic and cumin seeds, then cook for 1 more minute. Remove half the onion mixture and set to one side until ready to serve.

3 Add the turmeric, curry paste, tomatoes, cooked lentils and 150 ml (5 fl oz) water to the pan with the remaining onion mixture and heat through, stirring occasionally, then season. Serve the spiced lentils topped with the reserved fried onions and the coriander leaves.

 Freezing tip

This freezes very well so why not freeze individual portions, then defrost and reheat for a speedy supper or lunch?

Hungry family hint

For a non vegetarian option, top the spiced lentils with a 165 g (5¾ oz) **skinless boneless chicken breast** per person, grilled for 20 minutes until cooked through, for an extra 4 *ProPoints* values per serving.

Family friendly

Fragrant rice

Brown basmati rice has a lovely nutty flavour and texture without being too heavy and stodgy. Here, it is cooked with spices, which takes it to a new dimension.

Serves 4
Preparation time 5 minutes
Cooking time 25 minutes
5 *ProPoints* values per serving
20 *ProPoints* values per recipe

1 teaspoon cumin seeds
4 cardamom pods, split
200 g (7 oz) dried **brown basmati rice**
1 teaspoon turmeric
salt

1 Put the cumin seeds and cardamom in a dry, medium size, lidded saucepan over a medium heat then toast for 30 seconds until they start to smell aromatic. Remove from the heat and add the rice, 450 ml (16 fl oz) cold water and the turmeric. Season with a large pinch of salt, stir until everything is combined, and bring to the boil.

2 Turn the heat down to its lowest setting, cover, and simmer for 25 minutes.

3 When the rice is tender and all the water has been absorbed, remove the pan from the heat and leave to stand, still covered, for 5 minutes. Remove the cardamom and serve the rice.

Creamy vegetable pasanda

Serve with a Weight Watchers mini naan bread and 1 tablespoon **low fat plain yogurt** per person for an extra 4 *ProPoints* values per serving.

Serves 4
Preparation time 20 minutes
Cooking time 30 minutes
5 *ProPoints* values per serving
19 *ProPoints* values per recipe

calorie controlled cooking spray
2 **onions**, diced
3 **carrots**, peeled and sliced
400 g (14 oz) small **cauliflower** florets
4 **garlic cloves**, chopped finely
5 cm (2 inches) **fresh root ginger**, grated (no need to peel)
400 ml (14 fl oz) vegetable stock
4 tablespoons medium curry paste, such as balti
2 tablespoons tomato purée
200 g (7 oz) fine **green beans**, halved horizontally
25 g (1 oz) ground almonds
2 tablespoons reduced fat single cream
salt and freshly ground black pepper

1 Heat a large, lidded, heavy based saucepan over a medium heat. Spray with the cooking spray. Cook the onions, covered, for 5 minutes, until softened. Add the carrots, cauliflower, garlic and ginger, then cook, covered, for another 2 minutes.

2 Pour in the vegetable stock and stir in the curry paste and tomato purée. Bring to the boil, then reduce the heat and simmer, covered, for 20 minutes. Add the green beans and ground almonds, then cook for another 5–7 minutes until the vegetables are tender.

3 Season, stir in the cream and warm through before serving.

Fresh coconut chutney

Vibrant and zingy, this fresh chutney is perfect served with Lamb Shashlik (page 140), Coriander Fish with Crispy Ginger (page 122), Pork Vindaloo (page 134) or Minced Beef Bhuna (page 144).

Serves 4
10 minutes in total
2 *ProPoints* values per serving
11 *ProPoints* values per recipe

60 g (2 oz) desiccated, unsweetened coconut
juice of a lime
a large handful of **fresh mint** leaves
a large handful of **fresh coriander** leaves
1 teaspoon caster sugar
1 medium green **chilli**, de-seeded and chopped finely
salt

1 Put the coconut in a bowl and stir in 125 ml (4 fl oz) of water and the lime juice. Set to one side while you chop the herbs.
2 Stir the chopped mint, coriander, sugar and chilli into the coconut, then season with salt, to taste. Serve immediately.

 *Make ahead*

This fresh chutney will keep in the fridge for up to 1 day, if made in advance.

Chapatti

These flatbreads are so quick and easy to make, it would be wrong not to try them! They are best eaten straight after cooking, alongside a curry.

Makes 8
30 minutes in total + 15 minutes resting
2 *ProPoints* values per serving
19 *ProPoints* values per recipe

200 g (7 oz) wholemeal flour, plus ½ teaspoon for dusting
½ teaspoon salt
1 teaspoon low fat spread

1 Put the flour in a mixing bowl, then stir in the salt. Make a well in the centre and stir in 7 tablespoons of warm water with a fork, and then with your fingers, to make a smooth dough.
2 Turn the dough out on to a lightly floured surface and knead for 8 minutes until smooth and elastic. Put the dough back into the cleaned bowl, cover with cling film, then leave for 15 minutes to rest.
3 After the dough has rested, divide it into eight pieces and roll into balls. Roll out each piece of dough on a lightly floured surface into a round about the thickness of a 50 pence piece.
4 Heat a large, dry frying pan over a medium-high heat, until hot. Put one chapatti in the pan and cook for 1 minute on each side, turning the bread every 30 seconds, until puffed up and golden in places. Press down the chapatti occasionally with a spatula to ensure it cooks evenly.
5 Remove the chapatti to a plate, and keep warm, then repeat with the remaining dough. Stack the chapattis as you make them, spreading each with a little low fat spread and covering the stack with foil. Serve immediately.

With your fingers, make
a smooth dough.

Divide the dough into
eight and roll into balls.

Cook the bread until
puffed up and golden.

6 ProPoints value

12 ProPoints value

7 ProPoints value

9 ProPoints value

9 ProPoints value

Meals to
relax with

Nothing is more *pleasurable* than sitting down and having a *delicious* meal with friends and family. *Plan* your meals and *enjoy* every mouthful.

Great British breakfast

The beauty of this breakfast is that everything is cooked together in the oven. Serve it with a 44 g (1½ oz) slice of toasted wholemeal bread per person instead of the potato cakes for 3 *ProPoints* values per serving.

Serves 4
30 minutes in total
6 ProPoints values per serving
24 ProPoints values per recipe

250 g (9 oz) **mushrooms**
calorie controlled cooking spray
8 smoked **bacon medallions**
250 g (9 oz) cherry **tomatoes** on
  the vine
4 **eggs**
4 x 40 g (1½ oz) potato cakes
salt and freshly ground black pepper

1 Preheat the oven to Gas Mark 5/190°C/fan oven 170°C. Cover a large baking tray with foil. Put the mushrooms on a second piece of foil that is large enough to make a parcel. Spray the mushrooms with the cooking spray and season. Bring together the edges of the foil to make a parcel. Put the parcel on the foil-lined baking tray.

2 Put the bacon on the same tray as the mushrooms. Arrange the tomatoes around the edge. Spray the tomatoes with the cooking spray, put the tray in the oven and cook for 20 minutes until the bacon is starting to crisp and the tomatoes and mushrooms are tender.

3 After the bacon, tomato and mushrooms have been in the oven for 8 minutes, spray four holes of a deep non stick muffin tin with the cooking spray. Crack the eggs into the muffin tin, then season. Put the eggs in the oven with the bacon, tomatoes and mushrooms and cook for a further 10 minutes until the eggs are just set, the bacon is crisp and the tomatoes and mushrooms are tender.

4 While everything is in the oven, lightly toast the potato cakes until warmed through. Run a knife around the edge of each baked egg and ease them gently from the muffin tin. Serve the potato cakes with the bacon and baked eggs then put the tomatoes and mushrooms on the side.

V Veggie swap

Instead of the bacon medallions, use two **Quorn Deli Bacon Style Rashers** per person. Cook in the oven for 10–12 minutes, turning once. The *ProPoints* values will be 7 per serving.

Fold in the edges of the
foil to make a parcel.

Arrange the mushrooms,
bacon and tomatoes together.

Crack the eggs into a
muffin tray before cooking.

On the *ProPoints* plan,
you can enjoy the
weekend with a
fabulous fry-up.

Prawn kedgeree

This is a traditional British breakfast from colonial India, but it also makes a delicious lunch or supper dish. Although kedgeree normally includes smoked fish, this version features prawns for a delicious alternative.

Serves 2

40 minutes in total

10 *ProPoints* values per serving

19 *ProPoints* values per recipe

4 teaspoons mild curry powder

juice of ½ a lemon

125 g (4½ oz) frozen, peeled, raw king **prawns**, defrosted

100 g (3½ oz) dried **brown basmati rice**, washed

2 **eggs**

calorie controlled cooking spray

1 large **onion**, diced

2 large **garlic cloves**, chopped

75 g (2¾ oz) frozen **petit pois**

6 tablespoons vegetable stock

1 tablespoon chopped **fresh parsley**, to garnish (optional)

1 Mix together 1 teaspoon of the curry powder with 1 teaspoon of the lemon juice in a bowl. Pat the prawns dry with kitchen towel and add to the marinade, then turn until coated. Marinate, covered, in the fridge until ready to use, but not more than 1 hour.

2 Bring a large saucepan of water to the boil and cook the rice according to the packet instructions, then drain and rinse it under cold running water and leave to drain until ready to use. Meanwhile, to hard boil the eggs, put them in a pan and cover with cold water. Bring up to the boil, then turn down the heat slightly and gently boil the eggs for 8 minutes. Remove the eggs from the pan using a slotted spoon and place briefly under cold running water. Peel the shells from the eggs and set aside.

3 Heat a large, non stick, lidded frying pan over a medium heat and spray with the cooking spray. Cook the onion, covered, for 6 minutes, adding a splash of water if it becomes very dry. Add the garlic and cook, covered, for another 2 minutes. Add the petit pois and cook for 2 more minutes, stirring until softened.

4 Stir in the remaining curry powder, lemon juice, stock and cooked rice, and stir well until combined, cover, and heat through for a couple of minutes. Remove from the heat and set aside, covered, while you cook the prawns.

5 Heat a wok or non stick frying pan over a high heat. Spray with the cooking spray and stir-fry the prawns for 2 minutes until pink and cooked through.

6 Spoon the rice on to two plates, top with the prawns and 1 egg each, cut into quarters. Scatter the parsley over the top, if using.

V Veggie swap

For a vegetarian version, swap the prawns for 300 g (10½ oz) **Quorn Chicken Style Pieces**. Coat in the spices and add to the pan with the onion in Step 3, for 12 ***ProPoints*** values per serving.

Bubble and squeak cakes with eggs

These potato and veg cakes make a great brunch served with 100 g (3½ oz) **reduced sugar baked beans** per person for an extra 1 *ProPoints* value per serving.

Serves 4

40 minutes in total

5 *ProPoints* values per serving

20 *ProPoints* values per recipe

Ⓥ ❄ (bubble and squeak cakes only)

500 g (1 lb 2 oz) **potatoes**, peeled and cubed

calorie controlled cooking spray

100 g (3½ oz) **sprouts**, outer leaves removed, shredded finely

100 g (3½ oz) spring **cabbage**, outer leaves removed, shredded finely

4 **spring onions**, chopped finely

1 tablespoon flour, for dusting

4 **eggs**

salt and freshly ground black pepper

1 Place the potatoes in a medium lidded saucepan and cover with water. Bring to the boil, then reduce the heat and simmer for 10–15 minutes or until tender. Drain and return the potatoes to the pan. Place the pan on the turned off hot hob to dry, then mash until smooth.

2 Meanwhile, heat a large, non stick frying pan over a medium heat. Spray with the cooking spray and stir-fry the sprouts and cabbage for 5 minutes until just tender. Stir into the mashed potatoes with the spring onions. Season and mix well until combined. Cool the mixture. Tip the mixture on to a plate. Use the flour to dust your hands and a surface, then divide the mixture into four and form into round, flat patties, about 1 cm (½ inch) thick.

3 Clean the frying pan and spray with more cooking spray. Fry the potato cakes for 3 minutes on each side over a medium heat until golden. Set aside while you poach the eggs.

4 Heat a wide, shallow pan of water almost to boiling point, then turn down the heat to a gentle simmer. Crack an egg into a ramekin and gently tip the egg into the water. Add the other three eggs in the same way, then poach for 3 minutes until the whites are set but the yolks are still runny. Lift the eggs from the water with a slotted spoon and drain briefly on a kitchen towel.

5 Place a bubble and squeak cake on each plate and top with an egg. Season before serving.

Hungry family hint

Two 25 g (1 oz) slices lean back bacon per person, grilled until crisp, adds 2 *ProPoints* values per serving.

Make the most of any leftover veg from the weekend roast in this fabulous recipe.

Welsh rarebit bites

Here's a great quick snack for kids and they're a breeze to make. They could also be served for lunch with a large mixed leaf **salad**, dressed with 1 teaspoon of low calorie vinaigrette per person, for no extra *ProPoints* values per serving.

Serves 4

10 minutes in total

5 *ProPoints* values per serving

18 *ProPoints* values per recipe

8 x 2 cm (¾ inch) thick slices baguette
   (30 g (1¼ oz) per slice)

1 **egg**

1 teaspoon soy sauce

1 teaspoon English mustard

50 g (1¾ oz) half fat Cheddar cheese,
   grated

1 Preheat the grill to high. Put the slices of baguette under the grill until lightly toasted on one side.

2 Meanwhile, lightly beat the egg in a bowl and whisk in the soy sauce, mustard and Cheddar cheese. Remove the toast from the grill and spoon some of the cheese mixture on to the non grilled side of each. Grill for a further 2–3 minutes until slightly golden on top. Serve immediately.

More to spend?

Try a cheese and ham toastie. Cut four 35 g (1¼ oz) slices of ham in half. Place one half on top of each slice of toast before you add the cheese mixture and continue the recipe as in Step 2. Serve two toasties per person for an extra 1 *ProPoints* value per serving.

Cheese on toast –
what's not to love?

Family friendly

Fish fingers with minty mushy peas

A popular family meal, this adapted version is sure to be a big hit.

Serves 4

35 minutes in total

7 ProPoints values per serving

26 ProPoints values per recipe

calorie controlled cooking spray

2 tablespoons plain flour

1 large **egg**, beaten lightly

75 g (2¾ oz) natural breadcrumbs

1 tablespoon chopped **fresh parsley** or
  1 teaspoon paprika

500 g (1 lb 2 oz) thick skinless,
  boneless **white fish fillets**, patted
  dry and cut into 12 x 2 cm (¾ inch)
  wide fingers

salt and freshly ground black pepper

For the minty mushy peas

400 g (14 oz) frozen **petit pois**

juice of ½ a lemon

100 ml (3½ fl oz) hot vegetable stock

4 teaspoons extra light mayonnaise

5 tablespoons chopped **fresh mint**

1 Preheat the oven to Gas Mark 6/200°C/fan oven 180°C. Spray a non stick baking tray with the cooking spray.

2 Put the flour in a shallow bowl and season well. Beat the egg in a separate bowl. Put the breadcrumbs in a third bowl and stir in the parsley or paprika.

3 Dust each piece of fish in the flour until lightly coated. Next, dip the fish into the egg and then the breadcrumbs until evenly coated. Put the fish fingers on the baking tray and spray them with the cooking spray. Bake for 12–15 minutes, turning once, until the fish is cooked.

4 Meanwhile, add the petit pois to a medium saucepan of boiling water and simmer for 3–5 minutes, until tender. Drain and return to the pan with the lemon juice and stock. Roughly mash with a potato masher or the back of a fork until crushed. Put the mashed peas in a bowl, then stir in the mayonnaise and mint. Season to taste and serve with the fish fingers.

Hungry family hint

How about serving the fish fingers with a 100 g (3½ oz) portion of ready made potato wedges per person, cooked in the oven until crisp and golden, for an extra 5 **ProPoints** values per serving?

No-fuss fish pie

This simple fish pie uses a pre-packed mix of fresh fish, which you'll find in the fish section of the supermarket. It's coated in a creamy white sauce and is delicious served with steamed **broccoli**, for no extra *ProPoints* values.

Serves 2
Preparation time 25 minutes
Cooking time 25 minutes
10 *ProPoints* values per serving
19 *ProPoints* values per recipe
❄ (after baking, and only if using non pre-frozen fish)

250 g (9 oz) **potatoes**, peeled and diced into 2.5 cm (1 inch) cubes
1 **carrot**, peeled and sliced thinly
1 **onion**, sliced thinly
75 g (2¾ oz) fresh **spinach**
350 g (12 oz) **fish pie mix**, patted dry
1 tablespoon plain flour
125 g (4½ oz) low fat soft cheese
1 heaped teaspoon English mustard
1 tablespoon lemon juice
5 tablespoons **skimmed milk**
salt and freshly ground black pepper

1 Preheat the oven to Gas Mark 8/230°C/fan oven 210°C. Place the potatoes in a medium lidded saucepan and cover with water. Bring to the boil, reduce the heat and simmer for 10 minutes or until tender, then drain well. Return the potatoes to the pan, then briefly place on the turned off hot hob to dry. Season the potatoes, then mash until smooth.

2 Meanwhile, place the carrots and onions in a small saucepan of boiling water and simmer for about 4 minutes or until tender, then drain. Put the spinach in a steamer basket placed over a saucepan containing about 2.5 cm (1 inch) of water. Cover the steamer with a lid and bring the water to the boil. Reduce the heat and simmer for 1 minute or until the spinach is wilted and tender. Remove the spinach from the steamer and squeeze out any excess water. Set to one side.

3 Toss the fish pie mix with the flour and then put it in a 1.2 litre (2 pint) ovenproof dish with the carrot, onion and spinach. Mix together the low fat soft cheese, mustard, lemon juice and milk. Season and spoon the mixture over the fish and vegetables.

4 Spoon the mash on top, spreading it out to cover the fish mixture, and run a fork over the top to give it a slightly rough texture. Bake for 25 minutes, until the fish is cooked and the mash is golden on top.

 Try this

You can, of course, use your own choice of fish, but try to include a smoked fish in the mix for the best flavour.

Hungry family hint

A 40 g (1½ oz) slice of Irish soda bread per person will be delicious on the side for an extra 2 *ProPoints* values per serving.

By planning ahead, you can make sure you have everything you need to cook this simple fish pie.

Fish supper with homemade tartare

This recipe is a twist on the great British favourite, fish and chips, with sweet potato chips and crumb-coated baked fish. And of course, it's fab with 80 g (3 oz) **peas** per person for an extra 2 *ProPoints* values per serving.

Serves 4

40 minutes in total

9 *ProPoints* values per serving

34 *ProPoints* values per recipe

calorie controlled cooking spray

400 g (14 oz) **sweet potatoes**, peeled, cut in half and each half cut into long chips

1 **egg**

60 g (2 oz) fresh wholemeal breadcrumbs

finely grated zest of a large lemon

4 x 175 g (6 oz) **haddock** or **cod fillets**

salt and freshly ground black pepper

For the tartare sauce

4 tablespoons extra light mayonnaise

2 teaspoons lemon juice

2 teaspoons capers, drained and chopped finely

1 tablespoon chopped **fresh parsley**

1 Preheat the oven to Gas Mark 6/200°C/fan oven 180°C. Spray a large, non stick baking tray with the cooking spray. Place the chips on the tray and spray them with the cooking spray, then roast for 20 minutes on the top shelf.

2 Meanwhile, lightly beat the egg in a shallow bowl. Put the breadcrumbs on a plate, then mix in the lemon zest and season. Dip one side of each fish fillet into the egg and then the breadcrumbs, until it is coated. Spray a baking tray with the cooking spray and place the fish, breadcrumb-side up, on the tray. Spray the fish with more cooking spray.

3 Once the sweet potatoes have been in the oven for 20 minutes, turn them, spray with extra cooking spray and return them to the oven on the lower shelf. Put the fish in the oven at the same time on the top shelf and bake for 10–12 minutes until the fish is cooked and the chips are golden.

4 While the fish and chips are cooking, mix the ingredients for the tartare sauce. Serve the fish with the sweet potato chips and tartare sauce by the side.

 *Cook's tip*

To make your own breadcrumbs, put a slice of day-old bread in a mini chopper or food processor and whizz to make fine crumbs. The crumbs can be kept in the freezer then defrosted before use. This is a great way of using up any stale bread.

Hungry family hint

Half a can of mushy peas per person, heated until warmed through, will add 3 *ProPoints* values per serving.

Honey mustard chicken stew with herby dumplings

Warming and filling, this chicken dish makes a great change from Sunday roast on a cold day. Serve with steamed **spinach** and **courgettes** for no additional *ProPoints* values per serving.

Serves 4

Preparation time 40 minutes

Cooking time 25 minutes

9 *ProPoints* values per serving

37 *ProPoints* values per recipe

❄ (stew only)

calorie controlled cooking spray

600 g (1 lb 5 oz) **skinless boneless chicken breast pieces**

2 **onions**, chopped

2 **parsnips**, peeled and sliced

2 **carrots**, peeled and sliced

2 **fresh thyme** sprigs or 1 teaspoon dried thyme

2 bay leaves

150 ml (5 fl oz) dry white wine

250 ml (9 fl oz) vegetable stock

1 tablespoon wholegrain mustard

1 tablespoon clear honey

For the herby dumplings

110 g (4 oz) self-raising flour, plus extra for hands

a large pinch of bicarbonate of soda

2 teaspoons dried thyme

100 ml (3½ fl oz) **virtually fat free plain yogurt**

1 teaspoon English mustard

salt and freshly ground black pepper

1 To make the dumplings, mix together the flour, bicarbonate of soda and thyme, then season. Make a well in the centre and mix in the yogurt and mustard. Stir to make a firm dough. Set to one side, covered.

2 To make the stew, heat a large lidded casserole pan over a medium heat. Spray with the cooking spray and cook the chicken for 5 minutes until browned all over. You may need to cook it in two batches. Remove the chicken and set to one side.

3 Add the onions, parsnips and carrots, spray with more cooking spray, and cook for 5 minutes, covered, until softened. Stir the vegetables occasionally. Return the chicken to the casserole, add the thyme, bay leaves and wine and bring to the boil. Let the wine bubble away until it is reduced by half and there is no aroma of alcohol.

4 Meanwhile, dust your hands with a little flour, form the dumpling dough into eight dumplings and set aside.

5 Add the stock, mustard and honey to the casserole, stir well then bring to the boil. Reduce the heat, then place the dumplings in the casserole until they are half submerged in the liquid. Cover and simmer for 15 minutes, then remove the lid and cook for another 10 minutes until the dumplings are risen and fluffy and the chicken and vegetables are cooked.

Hungry family hint

A 225 g (8 oz) **potato**, baked in its skin, per person will really hit the spot and add 5 *ProPoints* values per serving.

Add the yogurt and
mustard to the flour.

Mix together to make
a firm dough.

Form the dough into
eight dumplings.

Cheat's chicken pies

The puff pastry topping and the creamy chicken sauce are cooked separately to speed up the cooking time, and then they are united just before serving to make a delicious 'pie'. Serve with steamed **broccoli** and **carrots** for no extra **ProPoints** values.

Serves 4

Preparation time 30 minutes +
  20 minutes soaking

Cooking time 15 minutes

9 ProPoints values per serving

38 ProPoints values per recipe

❄ (chicken and sauce only)

15 g (½ oz) dried porcini mushrooms

½ a kettleful of boiled water

calorie controlled cooking spray

600 g (1lb 5 oz) **skinless boneless chicken breasts**, cubed

1 large **leek**, sliced

250 g (9 oz) chestnut **mushrooms**

2 large **garlic cloves**, chopped

1 teaspoon dried thyme

175 ml (6 fl oz) dry white wine

125 g (4½ oz) low fat soft cheese

4 x 10 cm (4 inch) rounds light puff pastry, weighing 35 g (1¼ oz) each

1 tablespoon **skimmed milk**, to glaze

salt and freshly ground black pepper

chopped **fresh parsley**, to garnish (optional)

1 Soak the porcini mushrooms in 150 ml (5 fl oz) boiled water for 20 minutes until softened. Drain. Squeeze out any excess water from the mushrooms using the back of a spoon, then roughly chop them.

2 Preheat the oven to Gas Mark 6/200°C/fan oven 180°C. Heat a large, non stick, lidded saucepan over a medium heat. Spray with the cooking spray and cook the chicken for 5 minutes until browned all over. You may have to do this in two batches. Remove the chicken from the pan and set aside.

3 Spray the pan again and cook the leek for 3 minutes, covered, stirring occasionally. Add both types of mushroom, the garlic and thyme and cook, covered, for 3 minutes until softened.

4 Pour in the wine and let it bubble away, uncovered, for about 3 minutes until it has reduced and there is no smell of alcohol. Stir in the low fat soft cheese, return the chicken to the pan and simmer, covered, for 15 minutes, until the chicken is cooked. Season.

5 Meanwhile, spray a non stick baking tray with the cooking spray. Put the pastry circles on the tray, brush with the milk and prick each top three times. Bake for 12–15 minutes until golden and puffed up. Serve the chicken topped with the pastry and garnished with the parsley.

Hungry family hint

Roasted **potatoes** would go really well on the side. Turn on the oven in Step 1 and put 600 g (1 lb 5 oz) potatoes in a roasting tin. Spray the potatoes with the cooking spray and roast for 45 minutes, turning once, until golden and cooked through, for an extra 6 **ProPoints** values per serving.

Lemon, garlic and bay roast chicken

For a delightful summery dish, you could serve this with 100 g (3½ oz) boiled new **potatoes,** and a mixed leaf **salad,** dressed in lemon juice, with a tablespoon of extra light mayonnaise on the side per person for an extra 3 **ProPoints** values per serving. Garlic bread is another perfect extra for this chicken and a 26 g (1 oz) slice per person will add 3 **ProPoints** values per serving.

Serves 4

Preparation time 5 minutes

Cooking time 1 hour 15 minutes +
    15 minutes resting

5 ProPoints values per serving

52 ProPoints values per recipe

1 large lemon, cut in half

1.5 kg (3 lb 5 oz) chicken

4 bay leaves

1 head of **garlic,** cut in half crossways

calorie controlled cooking spray

salt and freshly ground black pepper

1 Preheat the oven to Gas Mark 4/180°C/fan oven 160°C. Slice one half of the lemon into four thin round slices.

2 Loosen the skin of the chicken and slip your hands under it and over the breast. Place the lemon slices and bay leaves under the skin. Put the remaining lemon half and the garlic in the chicken cavity. Spray the chicken all over with the cooking spray and season.

3 Place the chicken in a roasting tin and roast for 1 hour 15 minutes, occasionally basting the bird with the juices in the bottom of the tin.
To test whether the chicken is cooked, insert a skewer into the thickest part of the thigh. The chicken is ready when the juices run clear. If there is any trace of pinkness, return the chicken to the oven and cook for another 5 minutes. Repeat if necessary.

4 Remove the chicken from the oven and transfer to a warm plate, cover with foil, and leave to rest for 15 minutes. After the chicken has rested, carve, removing the skin, and serve 80 g (3 oz) per person.

More to spend?

Relax and enjoy a 125 ml (4 fl oz) glass of chilled dry white wine for an extra 3 **ProPoints** values per serving.

Enjoying a Sunday lunch with friends and family doesn't mean derailing your weight loss.

Pork and pear pot roast

Pot-roasting is a good way to keep meat moist during cooking and it works especially well with pork. Pears make a delicious alternative to the usual pork with apple.

Serves 4
Preparation time 30 minutes
Cooking time 1 hour 30 minutes
7 ProPoints values per serving
30 ProPoints values per recipe

600 g (1 lb 5 oz) **boneless loin of pork**, trimmed of visible fat
calorie controlled cooking spray
150 g (5 ½ oz) **shallots**, peeled and halved, if large
1 **onion**, sliced
2 **carrots**, peeled and sliced
1 **celery** stick, sliced
2 **garlic cloves**, chopped
1 teaspoon dried thyme
200 ml (7 fl oz) dry cider
150 ml (5 fl oz) vegetable stock
2 **pears**, peeled, cored and quartered
1–2 tablespoons **skimmed milk**
salt and freshly ground black pepper
a few sprigs of **fresh flat leaf parsley**, to garnish (optional)

1 Preheat the oven to Gas Mark 6/200°C/fan oven 180°C. Season the pork and spray with the cooking spray. Heat a lidded ovenproof casserole dish over a medium-high heat. Add the pork and brown on all sides. Remove and set to one side.

2 Add the shallots, onion, carrot, celery and garlic to the casserole, turn down the heat a little, and cook for 5 minutes until softened.

3 Return the pork to the casserole dish with the thyme, cider and stock. Season, then cover and put in the oven for 45 minutes. Add the pears to the casserole then return it to the oven and cook for a further 45 minutes or until the pork is cooked through and the pears have softened.

4 Remove the pork, vegetables and pears from the casserole dish with a slotted spoon and set aside, covered. Taste and season the juices, add the milk, then let it bubble away on the hob to thicken a little, if necessary.

5 Divide the pork equally between four, with two quarters of pear each, the vegetables, and a little sauce spooned over the top.

More to spend?

A 40 g (1½ oz) slice of crusty bread per person for mopping up the juices will add 3 **ProPoints** values per serving.

Yorkies with quick onion gravy

The secret to light, puffy Yorkshire puddings is to use a really hot tin and to avoid opening the oven door before they are ready. This gravy is thick and glossy and goes really well with roasted red meats.

Serves 6

35 minutes in total

4 *ProPoints* values per serving

27 *ProPoints* values per recipe

 (see Freezing tip)

50 g (1¾ oz) plain flour

1 **egg**, beaten lightly

150 ml (5 fl oz) **skimmed milk**

calorie controlled cooking spray

salt and freshly ground black pepper

For the onion gravy

300 ml (10½ fl oz) red wine

300 ml (10½ fl oz) chicken stock

125 g (4½ oz) caramelized onion
   chutney

2 teaspoons cornflour

1 To make the Yorkshire puddings, preheat the oven to Gas Mark 7/220°C/fan oven 200°C. Sift the flour into a bowl, make a well in the centre, and beat in the egg. Gradually whisk in the milk, drawing in the flour from the sides to make a smooth batter. Season and transfer the batter to a jug.

2 Put a six-hole non stick muffin tin in the oven for 5 minutes until really hot. Remove from the oven and, working quickly, spray each hole with the cooking spray and pour in the batter. Bake for 20–25 minutes until risen and golden. Serve immediately.

3 While the Yorkshire puddings are cooking, make the gravy. Pour the red wine into a pan and bring up to boiling point, then bubble away for 5 minutes until it has reduced and there is no aroma of alcohol. Add the chicken stock to the pan and return to the boil. Turn the heat down slightly and stir in the chutney.

4 Mix the cornflour with a little cold water to make a smooth mixture, then add to the gravy. Cook, stirring, for about 5 minutes until reduced, thickened and glossy. Serve the gravy with the Yorkshire puddings.

 Try this

Yorkshire puddings can also be served as a dessert. Serve each Yorkshire pudding with 1 tablespoon of half fat cream per person and drizzle each with 1 teaspoon of maple syrup or golden syrup for 3 **ProPoints** values per serving.

 Freezing tip

You can leave the Yorkshire puddings to cool, then freeze them for up to 1 month. Defrost first before reheating in an oven preheated to Gas Mark 6/200°C/fan oven 180°C for 5 minutes. The onion gravy will also freeze well for the same period of time.

Sausages with mustard mash

Tuck into this sausage and mash when you want a quick and delicious family meal. It goes well with carrots, cabbage or leeks for no additional *ProPoints* values per serving.

Serves 4

30 minutes in total

8 *ProPoints* values per serving

32 *ProPoints* values per recipe

❄ (parsley sauce only)

450 g pack sausages

450 g (1 lb) white **potatoes**, such as Maris Piper, peeled and cubed

1 tablespoon English mustard

salt and freshly ground black pepper

For the parsley sauce

25 g (1 oz) low fat spread

25 g (1 oz) plain flour

300 ml (10 fl oz) vegetable stock

4 tablespoons chopped **fresh parsley**

1 Preheat the grill to medium. Grill the sausages for 16–18 minutes, turning occasionally, until browned and cooked through.

2 Meanwhile, place the potatoes in a medium lidded saucepan and cover with water. Bring to the boil and simmer for 12–15 minutes or until tender. Drain the potatoes, then put them back in the pan over the turned off hob to dry for a minute. Add the mustard, season, then mash until smooth and keep warm, covered, while you make the parsley sauce.

3 To make the parsley sauce, melt the spread in a medium saucepan. Add the flour and cook for 1 minute, stirring continuously with a wooden spoon. Gradually add the stock, then bring to the boil, stirring continuously. Reduce the heat, add the parsley, season, then simmer until reduced and thickened.

4 Serve the mash, topped with the sausages and with the parsley sauce on the side.

Hungry family hint

A 20 g (½ oz) ready-made Yorkshire pudding per person adds 1 extra *ProPoints* value per serving.

Lamb steaks with roasted root vegetables

Winter root vegetables are fantastic roasted, taking on a lovely rich sweetness that goes particularly well with lamb.

Serves 2

Preparation time 15 minutes

Cooking time 40 minutes

11 *ProPoints* values per serving

22 *ProPoints* values per recipe

calorie controlled cooking spray

200 g (7 oz) **sweet potatoes**, peeled and cut into bite size chunks

1 large **onion**, peeled and cut into wedges

1 **carrot**, peeled and cut into 1 cm (½ inch) thick slices

1 **parsnip**, peeled and cut into 1 cm (½ inch) thick slices

6 **garlic cloves**, unpeeled

2 **fresh rosemary** sprigs, plus extra to garnish

1 tablespoon Worcestershire sauce

1 teaspoon wholegrain mustard

2 x 100 g (3½ oz) lean lamb steaks, trimmed of visible fat

salt and freshly ground black pepper

4 tablespoons extra light mayonnaise, to serve

1 Preheat the oven to Gas Mark 6/200°C/fan oven 180°C.

2 Spray a large, non stick baking tin with the cooking spray. Add the sweet potatoes, onions, carrot, parsnips, garlic and rosemary sprigs, spray with more cooking spray, pour over 2 tablespoons of water and roast in the oven for 35–40 minutes, turning once.

3 Meanwhile, mix together the Worcestershire sauce and mustard, season, and brush the mixture over both sides of the lamb steaks. Spray with the cooking spray.

4 When the vegetables have been in the oven for 30 minutes, heat a griddle or large, non stick frying pan over a medium-high heat. Cook the lamb for 3 minutes, turning once, or until cooked to your liking.

5 Remove the vegetables from the oven. Squeeze the garlic out of its papery skin into a bowl, squash with the back of a fork and stir in the mayonnaise. Serve the lamb with the vegetables by the side and a spoonful of the roasted garlic mayonnaise. Garnish with fresh rosemary, if liked.

Lancashire hot pot

This is perfect for a hearty family meal and you can dish it up with any of your favourite zero *ProPoints* value green vegetables.

Serves 4

Preparation time 35 minutes

Cooking time 1 hour 30 minutes

12 *ProPoints* values per serving

46 *ProPoints* values per recipe

 after cooking

calorie controlled cooking spray

450 g (1 lb) lamb neck fillet, trimmed of visible fat and cubed

2 **onions**, sliced

1 **celery** stick, chopped finely

4 **carrots**, peeled and sliced

200 g (7 oz) **mushrooms**, chopped roughly

25 g (1 oz) plain flour

400 ml (14 fl oz) chicken stock

2 teaspoons Worcestershire sauce

1 bay leaf

450 g (1 lb) **potatoes**, sliced very thinly into rounds (no need to peel)

salt and freshly ground black pepper

1 Heat a large, non stick, lidded saucepan over a medium heat. Spray with the cooking spray and cook half the lamb for 5 minutes until browned all over. Remove from the pan with a slotted spoon, then repeat with the remaining lamb. Set the lamb aside.

2 Preheat the oven to Gas Mark 4/180°C/fan oven 160°C. Add the onions to the pan, spray with more cooking spray, cover, and cook for 5 minutes, stirring occasionally, until softened. Add the celery, carrots and mushrooms and cook for another 2 minutes. Stir in the flour and cook, stirring constantly, for 2 minutes, then pour in the stock and Worcestershire sauce. Add the bay leaf and lamb, then season.

3 Transfer the lamb to a 23 x 28 cm (9 x 11 inch) ovenproof dish and arrange the potatoes on top, overlapping. Cover tightly with a lid or foil and cook in the oven for 1 hour. Remove the lid or foil, spray the top with the cooking spray, and cook for a further 20 minutes, uncovered. Turn the oven to a high grill and brown the top for a final 10 minutes.

Hungry family hint

Serve with a 225 g (8 oz) **potato**, baked in its skin, per person, cooked in the oven for 1 hour at the same time as you are cooking the hot pot, for an extra 5 ***ProPoints*** values per serving.

Add the flour. Cook and stir for 2 minutes.

Pour in the stock and Worcestershire sauce.

Arrange the potatoes over the top to cook.

Make planning your dinners one of your routines and enjoy this traditional favourite.

Spiced cottage pie with parsnip mash

A hearty, complete meal that breaks with the classic cottage pie with the addition of spices in the mince base and parsnips in the mash – it tastes great.

Serves 4

Preparation time 55 minutes

Cooking time 20 minutes

8 **ProPoints** values per serving

30 **ProPoints** values per recipe

calorie controlled cooking spray

2 **onions**, chopped

2 **carrots**, peeled and grated coarsely

1 **celery** stick, chopped finely

125g (4½ oz) **mushrooms**, sliced thinly

3 **garlic cloves**, chopped

300 g (10½ oz) lean beef mince

1 tablespoon mild curry powder

1 tablespoon tomato purée

100 g (3½ oz) frozen **petit pois**

1 beef stock cube

325 g (11½ oz) **potatoes**, peeled and cut into even-sized chunks

275 g (9½ oz) **parsnips**, peeled and cut into even-sized chunks

salt and freshly ground black pepper

1 Heat a large, non stick, lidded saucepan over a medium heat and spray with the cooking spray. Cook the onions, covered, for 6 minutes until softened. Add the carrots, celery, mushrooms and garlic, spray again, and cook for another 5 minutes, until softened.

2 Meanwhile, heat a large lidded non stick frying pan over a medium heat, and add the mince, curry powder and tomato purée. Bring to the boil, then reduce the heat to low and simmer, part-covered, for 10 minutes, stirring occasionally. Add the petit pois, stir and return the lid, then cook for another 5 minutes until browned all over, stirring to break up any lumps of meat.

3 Dissolve the beef stock cube in 300 ml (10 fl oz) hot water and pour this into the pan with the vegetables. Add the mince mixture. Bring to the boil, then reduce the heat to low and simmer, part-covered, for 15 minutes, then season.

4 Preheat the oven to Gas Mark 4/180°C/fan oven 160°C. Meanwhile, place the potatoes and parsnips in a medium lidded saucepan and cover with water. Bring to the boil and simmer for 10–15 minutes until tender. Drain and return to the pan then place on the turned off hot hob to let them dry slightly. Season and mash the potatoes and parsnips until smooth.

5 Put the mince mixture into a 1.7 litre (3 pint) deep ovenproof dish and top with the mash – you want the top to be quite rough so it browns nicely. Cook in the oven for 20 minutes until the top is golden.

 Freezing tip

Cottage pie freezes well and you could try freezing individual portions before baking. They will freeze for up to 1 month. Make sure you defrost thoroughly before cooking, following Step 5.

Beef, ale and mushroom pie

The rich beef filling for this pie takes a little while to cook to ensure the meat is melt-in-the-mouth tender, but it needs a minimum of attention. Serve with **string beans,** steamed red **cabbage** or **leeks** for no additional *ProPoints* values per serving.

Serves 6

Preparation time 25 minutes

Cooking time 1 hour 20 minutes

10 *ProPoints* values per serving

60 *ProPoints* values per recipe

 (beef stew only)

1 heaped tablespoon plain flour

500 g (1lb 2 oz) **lean diced braising steak**, cut into bite size chunks

calorie controlled cooking spray

2 **onions**, sliced

3 **carrots**, peeled and sliced

2 **turnips**, peeled and chopped

200 g (7 oz) chestnut **mushrooms**, quartered

2 large **garlic cloves**, chopped roughly

1 teaspoon dried thyme

2 bay leaves

400 ml (14 fl oz) brown ale

400 ml (14 fl oz) beef stock

275 g (9½ oz) ready-rolled light shortcrust pastry

2 teaspoons **skimmed milk**

salt and freshly ground black pepper

1 Put the flour on a plate and season. Add the beef and turn the meat until it is dusted in the flour. Heat a large lidded casserole dish and spray with the cooking spray. Add the beef and cook for about 6 minutes until browned all over.

2 Add the onions, carrots, turnips, mushrooms, garlic, thyme and bay leaves and turn until combined. Pour in the ale and stock and bring to the boil. Turn the heat down slightly and simmer, part-covered, for 1 hour 20 minutes, until the liquid has reduced and thickened and the meat is tender. Stir occasionally to prevent the stew from sticking to the bottom of the pan.

3 Preheat the oven to Gas Mark 5/190°C/fan oven 170°C. Season the stew and transfer it to a 23 x 28 cm (9 x 11 inch) pie dish. Brush the rim of the pie dish with water. Cut a 1 cm (½ inch) strip of pastry and place it around the rim of the dish. Cut the remaining pastry to fit and place over the top of the dish with a slight overhang, then press the edges together using the back of a fork.

4 Brush the top of the pie with the milk, prick the top with a fork, and bake for 25 minutes until the pastry is cooked and golden.

Hungry family hint

Serve with a 150 g (5½ oz) baked **sweet potato** per person for an extra 4 *ProPoints* values per serving. Heat the oven in Step 2 before you assemble the pie and cook the sweet potatoes for 45 minutes, until tender in the centre.

Steak with colcannon

Colcannon is a traditional mash flavoured with spring onions, cabbage and leek. It goes particularly well with pan-fried steak. If you have time, remove the steak from the fridge about an hour before cooking to allow it to come up to room temperature. Serve with boiled **carrots** for no extra *ProPoints* values.

Serves 4

25 minutes in total

8 *ProPoints* values per serving

31 ***ProPoints*** values per recipe

425 g (15 oz) **potatoes**, peeled and cut into chunks

150 g (5½ oz) sweetheart **cabbage** or **kale**, shredded finely

1 **leek**, sliced thinly

6 **spring onions**, sliced thinly

calorie controlled cooking spray

4 x 140 g (5 oz) **lean fillet steaks**

salt and freshly ground black pepper

fresh coriander sprigs, to garnish, (optional)

1 Put the potatoes in a medium lidded saucepan and cover with water. Bring to the boil and simmer for about 10 minutes or until tender. Drain and return to the pan, then place briefly on the turned off hot hob, to allow the potatoes to dry out slightly. Season the potatoes and mash until smooth.

2 Meanwhile, put the cabbage, leek and spring onions in a medium size lidded saucepan, spray with the cooking spray, and add 1 tablespoon of water. Cook over a medium heat, covered, for 5 minutes or until tender. Stir the vegetables regularly. Stir the vegetables into the mash until combined, then cover to keep warm.

3 Spray each side of the steaks with the cooking spray and season. Heat a griddle or large, non stick frying pan and cook the steaks two at a time for 2 minutes on each side, turning every minute, or until cooked to your liking. Cover the first batch with foil to keep warm while you cook the second batch.

4 Spoon the mash on to four plates and serve with the steak, drizzling over any juices from the pan. Garnish with the coriander, if using.

 Try this

Colcannon also goes really well with a 140 g (5 oz) **lean gammon steak** per person, instead of the fillet steak, for 7 ***ProPoints*** values per serving. Cook two steaks at a time for 3–4 minutes on each side. Cover the first batch with foil to keep warm while you cook the second batch.

More to spend?

Accompany each serving with 1 tablespoon of horseradish sauce per person for an extra 1 ***ProPoints*** value per serving.

Chill out
desserts & bakes

Following the **ProPoints** plan doesn't mean you can't *enjoy* something *sweet* after dinner. Remember, you have your weekly *allowance* to fit around *your week* to use whenever you need it.

Lemon meringue semifreddo

This incredibly delicious, light and creamy yogurt ice is flavoured with lemon curd and pieces of meringue and really does taste just like lemon meringue pie! Be sure to use a thick yogurt for the best results.

Serves 10

15 minutes in total + 6 hours freezing
   + 20 minutes thawing

3 *ProPoints* values per serving

26 *ProPoints* values per recipe

2 **eggs**, separated

50 g (1¾ oz) caster sugar

250 ml (9 fl oz) **0% fat Greek yogurt**

250 ml (9 fl oz) thick **low fat natural yogurt**

grated zest of a large lemon

60 g (2 oz) lemon curd

4 x 14 g meringue nests, broken into large pieces (about 2.5 cm/1 inch)

1 Line the base and sides of a 900 g (2 lb) loaf tin with a double layer of cling film, leaving an overhang.

2 Whisk together the egg yolks and sugar for about 3 minutes until they are pale and creamy and the beaters leave a trail for a few seconds when they are lifted. Stir the Greek yogurt, bio yogurt, lemon zest and lemon curd into the egg yolk mixture until smooth and evenly blended.

3 Wash the whisk thoroughly and whisk the egg whites in a clean, grease-free bowl for about 2 minutes until they form stiff peaks. Using a metal spoon, fold them gently into the yogurt mixture.

4 Gently fold in half of the meringue, without breaking up the pieces. Pour the mixture into the loaf tin, level the top, then cover with the excess cling film. Freeze for 6 hours until frozen.

5 Remove from the freezer 20 minutes before serving. To serve, unwrap the top of the cling film and turn the semifreddo out on to a serving plate. Peel off the cling film, and scatter the remaining crushed meringues over the top. Cut into 2 cm (¾ inch) thick slices and serve.

 Cook's tip

You can return any leftover semifreddo to the freezer. Wrap again in cling film and freeze for up to 1 month.

Whisk together the egg yolks and sugar.

Fold the meringue gently into the yogurt mixture.

Pour the mixture into a loaf tin and level the top.

Cherry meringue pies

A twist on a popular classic, this version features a meringue topping which simply needs flashing under a hot grill.

Serves 4

15 minutes in total + 15 minutes
  chilling

4 *ProPoints* values per serving

15 *ProPoints* values per recipe

75 g (2¾ oz) light digestive biscuits

25 g (1 oz) low fat spread

350 g (12 oz) frozen stoned dark
  cherries, defrosted

1 teaspoon caster sugar

1 slightly heaped teaspoon cornflour

For the meringue topping

1 large **egg white**

1 tablespoon caster sugar

1 Crush the biscuits in a blender or put them in a plastic bag and crush with the end of a rolling pin until they become fine crumbs. Put the biscuit crumbs in a bowl. Melt the spread and mix it into the crumbs. Divide the mixture between four large (150 ml/5 fl oz) ramekins and press with the back of a teaspoon to form firm bases. Set to one side.

2 Put the defrosted cherries and sugar in a saucepan. Spoon out a little of the juice from the cherries into a small bowl and stir in the cornflour. Heat the cherries and, when warm, stir in the cornflour mixture and cook for 2 minutes over a medium-low heat until the juice has thickened. Using a hand-blender, partially blend the cherries to a coarse purée, then spoon the mixture on top of the biscuit bases and chill for 15 minutes.

3 Preheat the grill to medium high. Put the egg white in a clean, grease-free bowl and whisk until it forms stiff peaks. Add the sugar and whisk to a firm, glossy meringue. Spoon a quarter of the meringue on top of each ramekin in a peak shape.

4 Put the ramekins on a baking tray and place under the grill for 1 minute until they start to turn golden in places — take care as they can easily burn. Remove from the heat and leave to cool for a couple of minutes before serving.

More to spend?

If you're feeling indulgent, serve with 1 tablespoon of light single cream per person for an extra 1 ***ProPoints*** value per serving.

Press the biscuit crumbs
with a spoon for a firm base.

Spoon the cherry mixture
over the biscuit bases.

Spoon on the meringue
in a peak shape.

These are perfect for
when you want something
sweet after a meal but
don't have a lot of *ProPoints*
allowance left.

Family friendly

Tropical baked bananas

These couldn't be simpler to make. For the best flavour, make sure the bananas are ripe, but not overly soft, because you want them to hold their shape when baked.

Serves 4
25 minutes in total
1 ProPoints value per serving
3 ProPoints values per recipe

4 ripe **bananas**, peeled
435 g can crushed **pineapple in natural juice**, drained,
  2 tablespoons pineapple juice reserved
4 teaspoons desiccated unsweetened coconut
½ teaspoon ground nutmeg

1 Preheat the oven to Gas Mark 5/190°C/fan oven 170°C. Place each banana on a piece of foil that is large enough to make a parcel.
2 Mix the crushed pineapple with the reserved juice from the can. Spoon the pineapple mixture over the bananas.
3 Bring together the edges of each piece of the foil and scrunch them together to make four parcels. Place the parcels on a baking tray and bake for 18–20 minutes until the bananas have softened.
4 While the bananas are baking, put the coconut in a dry, non stick frying pan and toast for about 2 minutes, stirring occasionally, until beginning to turn golden. Remove from the heat and transfer to a bowl.
5 Open the foil parcels and serve the bananas nestled in the foil, sprinkled with the coconut and a little ground nutmeg.

Deep apple pie

Enjoy with 1 tablespoon of half fat single cream per person for an extra 1 **ProPoints** value per serving.

Serves 8
Preparation time 15 minutes
Cooking time 30 minutes
2 ProPoints values per serving
17 ProPoints values per recipe
 (freeze after baking)

4 eating **apples**, peeled, halved, cored and sliced thinly
1 teaspoon ground mixed spice or cinnamon
1 teaspoon caster sugar
a squeeze of lemon juice
135 g (5 oz) light ready-to-roll shortcrust pastry
2 teaspoons **skimmed milk**, to glaze

1 Preheat the oven to Gas Mark 5/190°C/fan oven 170°C. Put the apples in a lidded pan and cover with 3 tablespoons of water. Cover and cook the apples over a medium heat for 5 minutes until softened.
2 Transfer the apples to a 19 cm (7½ inch) pie dish. Sprinkle with the mixed spice and sugar, then add a squeeze of lemon juice. Turn the apples until everything is mixed together.
3 Remove the pastry from the fridge and roll out slightly to fit the top of the pie dish. Wet the rim of the pie dish with water and top with the pastry. Crimp the edges using a fork and prick the centre a few times.
4 Brush the top with the milk. Bake for 25–30 minutes until the pastry is cooked and golden. Leave to stand for a couple of minutes to cool before serving, in wedges.

 Try this
Instead of apple, you could fill this pie with a combination of **pears** and **blackberries**. Peel, core and slice four just-ripe pears and combine with 250 g (9 oz) blackberries. The **ProPoints** values per serving will be the same.

Sprinkle the apples with
mixed spice and sugar.

Wet the rim of the dish
and top with the pastry.

Crimp the edges of the
pastry and prick the top.

Marmalade bread and butter pudding

The ultimate comfort pudding, this family favourite is best made with slightly stale bread. It's extra good with 1 tablespoon of **0% fat Greek yogurt** per person for no extra *ProPoints* values per serving.

Serves 6
Preparation time 10 minutes
Cooking time 25 minutes
5 *ProPoints* values per serving
28 *ProPoints* values per recipe

9 slices **Weight Watchers sliced white bread**,
   day-old, crusts removed
20 g (¾ oz) low fat spread
60 g (2 oz) smooth marmalade
400 ml (14 fl oz) **skimmed milk**
2 **eggs**
2 tablespoons caster sugar
1 teaspoon vanilla extract
2 teaspoons ground ginger

1 Spread the bread with the low fat spread and then the marmalade. Cut each slice in half diagonally, then arrange in a 26 x 20 cm (10½ x 8 inch) ovenproof dish in two rows.
2 Preheat the oven to Gas Mark 4/180°C/fan oven 160°C. Heat the milk until it just reaches boiling point.
3 Whisk the eggs, sugar, vanilla extract and ground ginger together in a large bowl until frothy. Gradually pour the milk into the egg mixture, whisking to make a thin custard.
4 Pour the mixture over the bread and press the bread gently into the custard mixture until submerged. Bake for 25 minutes until the custard is just set and the top is golden in places.

Quick summer pudding

This well loved dessert is reminiscent of summer with its vibrant red and purple berries. Serve with 2 tablespoons of fat free vanilla yogurt or 1 tablespoon of reduced fat single cream per person, for an extra 1 *ProPoints* value per serving.

Serves 6
15 minutes in total + 1 hour resting
4 *ProPoints* values per serving
22 *ProPoints* values per recipe

500 g (1 lb 2 oz) mixed frozen **summer fruit**
juice of 2 oranges
3 tablespoons caster sugar
12 slices **Weight Watchers sliced white bread**, crusts removed

1 Put the summer fruit, orange juice and caster sugar in a saucepan over a medium-low heat and simmer for 5 minutes until the fruit has defrosted. Strain the fruit over a bowl to catch the juice (see Step 2).
2 Put six slices of the bread into a 23 x 28 cm (9 x 11 inch) dish to cover the base. Spoon the berries over the bread, spreading them out in an even layer. Spoon a third of the juice over the top, making sure all the bread is soaked in the berry juice.
3 Arrange the remaining bread in a single layer on top, then spoon the remaining juice over the bread until it is completely soaked in the juice. Cover with a sheet of baking paper or cling film, press down, then weigh down with cans and chill for 1 hour until firm. Cut into six portions to serve.

Strain the summer fruit over a bowl.

Spoon the berries over the bread and spread them out.

Spoon the remaining juice over the bread.

Cook with kids

Peach crumbles

These individual peach crumbles make a simple pudding. You could serve them with 2 tablespoons of thick **low fat natural yogurt** per person for an extra 1 *ProPoints* value per serving.

Serves 4
Preparation time 10 minutes
Cooking time 15 minutes
3 ProPoints values per serving
12 ProPoints values per recipe

4 gingernut biscuits
20 g (¾ oz) toasted flaked almonds, chopped finely
  (See Cook's tip)
20 g (¾ oz) low fat spread
4 ripe but firm **peaches**, cut in half horizontally and stoned

1 Preheat the oven to Gas Mark 4/180°C/fan oven 160°C.
2 Put the biscuits in a plastic food bag and crush with the end of a rolling pin to make coarse crumbs. Transfer the crumbs to a bowl and stir in the almonds. Using the back of a teaspoon, rub the spread into the almond and biscuit crumbs to make a rough crumble.
3 In each peach half, spoon the crumble mixture into a heap inside the cavity left by the stone. Place the peaches in a baking dish and bake for 15 minutes until the crumble topping is slightly crisp and the peaches are tender.

 *Cook's tip*
If you can't find ready-toasted almonds, toast flaked almonds in a dry, non stick frying pan for 2 minutes, shaking the pan occasionally, until they begin to turn golden.

Coconut drops

These lovely little coconut macaroons are so quick and simple to make and will keep for up to 5 days stored in an airtight tin – if they last that long!

Makes 15
Preparation time 5 minutes
Cooking time 12 minutes
2 ProPoints values per serving
25 ProPoints values per recipe

½ teaspoon low fat spread, for greasing
3 **egg whites**
40 g (1½ oz) caster sugar
110 g (4 oz) desiccated unsweetened coconut

1 Preheat the oven to Gas Mark 6/200°C/fan oven 180°C. Lightly grease two non stick baking trays with the low fat spread or line the trays with non stick baking paper and grease with low fat spread.
2 Lightly whisk the egg whites in a large mixing bowl until they are frothy and bubbly, then stir in the caster sugar and desiccated coconut until combined.
3 Place 15 tablespoonfuls of the coconut mixture on the baking trays and flatten the tops slightly with the back of a spoon. Bake for 10–12 minutes until just beginning to turn golden.
4 Leave the coconut drops to cool slightly for a couple of minutes to firm up before transferring them to a wire rack to cool completely.

Banana cinnamon muffins

These gorgeous fruity muffins certainly go down well with kids and adults alike.

Makes 16
Preparation time 10 minutes
Cooking time 15 minutes
2 ProPoints values per serving
38 ProPoints values per recipe

225 g (8 oz) self-raising flour
1 teaspoon baking powder
½ teaspoon bicarbonate of soda
100 g (3½ oz) caster sugar
a pinch of salt
1 teaspoon ground cinnamon
2 large ripe **bananas**, 275 g (9½ oz) peeled weight
2 **eggs**
75 g (2¾ oz) half fat crème fraîche
1 teaspoon vanilla extract
2 tablespoons **skimmed milk**

1 Preheat the oven to Gas Mark 4/180°C/fan oven 160°C. Line a 16-hole muffin tin with paper cases (or use two smaller tins).
2 Mix together the flour, baking powder, bicarbonate of soda, caster sugar, salt and cinnamon in a mixing bowl.
3 Mash the bananas in a separate bowl and stir in the eggs, crème fraîche, vanilla extract and milk.
4 Make a well in the centre of the flour mixture, add the banana mixture and stir roughly with a wooden spoon until just combined (it doesn't matter if the mixture is lumpy – you don't want to over-mix it or the muffins will be tough).
5 Spoon the mixture into the paper cases and bake for 12–15 minutes until the muffins are risen and light golden. Transfer to a wire rack to cool.

Strawberry posset

This delightfully creamy, fruity dessert is so simple to make, yet so pleasing to eat.

Serves 4
15 minutes in total + 30 minutes chilling
2 ProPoints values per serving
6 ProPoints values per recipe

450 g (1 lb) **strawberries**, hulled
2 large **egg whites**
2 tablespoons caster sugar
2 teaspoons vanilla extract
125 ml (4 fl oz) thick **low fat natural yogurt**

1 Reserve eight strawberries and purée the rest in a blender – or you could use a hand-held blender, but you may have to do this in batches.
2 Whisk the egg whites in a clean, grease-free bowl for about 1 minute until they form soft peaks. Gradually whisk in the caster sugar until the mixture forms stiff, glossy peaks.
3 Mix together the vanilla extract and yogurt, then gradually fold in the egg whites using a metal spoon, to keep as much air in the mixture as possible.
4 Fold in the strawberry purée to make lovely swirls of the fruit. Spoon the mixture into four glasses and chill for 30 minutes. Serve, decorated with the reserved strawberries.

More to spend?

For a treat, enjoy with a 20 g (½ oz) all butter shortbread biscuit per person for an extra 3 **ProPoints** values per serving.

Cook with kids

2 ProPoints value

2 ProPoints value

Strawberry and cream cupcakes

Everyone will love these cupcakes with their vanilla cream and fresh strawberry topping.

Makes 12

Preparation time 15 minutes

Cooking time 15 minutes

3 _ProPoints_ values per serving

38 _ProPoints_ values per recipe

Ⓥ ❄ (plain cakes only)

100 g (3½ oz) self-raising flour

½ teaspoon baking powder

100 g (3½ oz) caster sugar

100 g (3½ oz) low fat spread

2 **eggs**, beaten lightly

1 teaspoon vanilla extract

2 tablespoons **skimmed milk**

For the vanilla cream

75 g (2¾ oz) low fat soft cheese

1 teaspoon vanilla extract

2 teaspoons icing sugar

6 **strawberries**, halved

1 Preheat the oven to Gas Mark 4/180°C/fan oven 160°C. Place 12 paper cases in a bun tin.

2 Sift the flour and baking powder into a large mixing bowl, then stir in the sugar. Add the low fat spread, eggs, vanilla extract and milk to the flour mixture. Using an electric hand whisk or wooden spoon, beat everything together for 3 minutes or until the cake mixture is light and fluffy.

3 Spoon the mixture into the paper cases and bake for 12–15 minutes until risen and light golden. Leave to cool in the bun tin for a couple of minutes, then remove and cool on a wire rack.

4 To make the vanilla cream, mix together the soft cheese, vanilla extract and icing sugar until smooth and creamy. Spread some of the icing over the top of each cake and finish with half a strawberry.

 *Try this*

For chocolate cupcakes, replace 1 tablespoon of the self-raising flour with the same quantity of cocoa powder. You could also dust the vanilla cream topping with a little extra cocoa powder and top with a fresh **raspberry** for the same **_ProPoints_** values per cupcake.

More to spend?

For a grown-up treat, what could be nicer than a Strawberry and Cream Cupcake with a chilled 125 ml (4 fl oz) glass of prosecco per person for an additional 3 **_ProPoints_** values per serving?

Cheat's chocolate brownies

Nobody can resist these wonderfully chocolatey brownies, and, unusually, they are made with mayonnaise, rather than butter or spread! Look for chocolate with around 70% cocoa solids for the best flavour.

Makes 16
Preparation time 15 minutes
Cooking time 25 minutes
3 *ProPoints* values per serving
49 *ProPoints* values per recipe
V

½ teaspoon low fat spread
75 g (2¾ oz) dark chocolate, about
   70% cocoa solids, broken into
   even-sized pieces
75 g (2¾ oz) plain flour
¼ teaspoon bicarbonate of soda
150 g (5½ oz) caster sugar
25 g (1 oz) cocoa powder
2 **eggs**, separated
100 g (3½ oz) extra light mayonnaise
1 teaspoon vanilla extract
2 tablespoons **skimmed milk**

1 Preheat the oven to Gas Mark 4/180°C/fan oven 160°C. Line the base of an 18 cm (7 inch) square cake tin with baking paper and grease the sides with the low fat spread.

2 Fill a medium size saucepan with about 4 cm (1½ inches) of hot water. Put the chocolate in a heatproof bowl and rest the bowl on top of the pan so it fits snugly – do not let the water touch the bottom of the bowl. Bring the water to a gentle simmer and heat the chocolate, stirring occasionally until it has melted. Carefully remove the bowl from the pan and let the melted chocolate cool slightly.

3 Sift the flour and bicarbonate of soda into a large mixing bowl. Reserving 1 teaspoon of the cocoa powder, stir the rest into the mixture, then stir in the sugar.

4 Beat together the egg yolks, mayonnaise, vanilla extract and milk in a separate bowl, then stir this mixture into the flour mixture. Stir in the melted chocolate.

5 Whisk the egg whites in a clean, grease-free bowl for about 1 minute, until they form soft peaks, then carefully fold them into the chocolate mixture with a metal spoon.

6 Pour the mixture into the tin, spread into an even layer and bake for 20–25 minutes until the cake is risen and just firm. Leave to cool in the tin, then turn out and cut into 16 pieces.

 Try this

Serve warm with a 60 g (2 oz) scoop of reduced fat vanilla ice cream per person for an extra 2 ***ProPoints*** values per serving.

Melt the chocolate
in a heatproof bowl
over a pan.

Stir the melted chocolate
into the egg and
flour mixture.

Pour the mixture into
the tin and spread
in an even layer.

Mixed spice, apple and oat biscuits

Makes 12

Preparation time 10 minutes

Cooking time 20 minutes

2 *ProPoints* values per serving

23 *ProPoints* values per recipe

75 g (2¾ oz) low fat spread, plus ½ teaspoon for greasing

60 g (2 oz) rolled **oats**

75 g (2¾ oz) wholemeal flour

a pinch of salt

½ teaspoon bicarbonate of soda

1 teaspoon ground mixed spice

75 g (2¾ oz) apple sauce from a jar

1 Preheat the oven to Gas Mark 5/190°C/fan oven 170°C. Lightly grease two non stick baking trays with a little of the spread.

2 Mix together the oats, flour, salt, bicarbonate of soda and mixed spice in a large mixing bowl.

3 Cream the low fat spread in a separate bowl and beat in 50 g (1¾ oz) of the apple sauce, adding it a little at a time. Gradually fold in the oat mixture.

4 Place 12 heaped tablespoonfuls of the mixture on the prepared baking trays, spacing them apart. Flatten them slightly with the back of a fork. Bake for 15–20 minutes until beginning to turn golden.

5 Leave on the baking trays for a couple of minutes, then cool on a wire rack. Just before serving, spoon a little of the remaining apple sauce on top of each biscuit.

 *Cook's tip*

The biscuits will keep for up to 5 days in an airtight container. Add the apple sauce topping just before serving.

Marmalade and ginger cookies

These mini cookies are similar to flapjacks and are just the thing if you're looking for a little bit of sweetness.

Makes 23

Preparation time 10 minutes

Cooking time 15 minutes

2 *ProPoints* values per serving

39 *ProPoints* values per recipe

50 g (1¾ oz) plain flour

¼ teaspoon bicarbonate of soda

1 teaspoon ground ginger

150 g (5½ oz) rolled **oats**

50 g (1¾ oz) low fat spread

75 g (2¾ oz) light soft brown sugar

finely grated zest of an orange

1 **egg**, beaten lightly

50 g (1¾ oz) marmalade

1 Preheat the oven to Gas Mark 4/180°C/fan oven 160°C and line two baking trays with baking paper.

2 Mix together the flour, bicarbonate of soda and ginger in a bowl and stir in the oats.

3 In a separate bowl, beat the spread and sugar together until pale and creamy, using a wooden spoon. Beat in the orange zest, egg and marmalade until smooth. (An electric whisk makes easy work of this.) Stir in the flour mixture and mix well.

4 Place 23 tablespoonfuls of the mixture on the baking sheets, spaced 2.5 cm (1 inch) apart, then flatten the tops slightly with the back of the spoon. Bake the cookies for 12–15 minutes or until slightly crisp and golden. Transfer to a wire rack to cool.

Honey, orange and almond cake

This is similar to the traditional Spanish Santiago cake, with its wonderful orange flavour and sticky honey topping. It's also gluten-free.

Makes 1 cake (10 slices)

Preparation time 20 minutes +
   20 minutes cooling

Cooking time 40 minutes

5 *ProPoints* values per serving

53 *ProPoints* values per recipe

V

½ teaspoon low fat spread, for greasing

6 **eggs**, separated

100 g (3½ oz) caster sugar

grated zest of 3 oranges and juice
   of ½ an orange

150 g (5½ oz) ground almonds

To decorate

juice of 1½ oranges

2 tablespoons clear honey

1 **orange**, peeled and cut into
   thin rounds

1 Preheat the oven to Gas Mark 4/180°C/fan oven 160°C. Line the base of a 20 cm (8 inch) springform cake tin with baking paper and lightly grease the sides with the low fat spread. Beat together the egg yolks, caster sugar, orange zest, the juice of half of an orange and the ground almonds in a large mixing bowl.

2 Whisk the egg whites in a separate clean, grease-free bowl for about 2 minutes until they form stiff peaks. Fold a spoonful into the cake mixture to loosen it, then fold in the remaining egg whites, using a metal spoon. Carefully pour the mixture into the prepared cake tin. Bake for 35–40 minutes or until a skewer inserted into the centre of the cake comes out clean. Leave to cool in the tin for about 20 minutes.

3 To make the topping, put the orange juice and honey in a small pan and bring to the boil, stir once, then cook without stirring for 6–8 minutes until reduced and syrupy.

4 Remove the cake from the tin and, using a fork, prick the top all over, then spoon three-quarters of the syrup over the top. Arrange the orange slices on top of the cake and spoon over the remaining syrup. Let the syrup soak into the cake for a few minutes and then serve, cut into slices.

More to spend?

Serve with a tablespoon of **virtually fat free plain fromage frais** per person for an extra 1 ***ProPoints*** value per serving.

Dorset pear cake

This cake has a layer of cinnamon-coated pieces of pear running through the centre, which gives a delicious bit of fruitiness with every bite.

Makes 12 slices

Preparation time 15 minutes

Cooking time 50 minutes

4 ProPoints values per serving

46 ProPoints values per recipe

100 g (3½ oz) low fat spread, plus
  ½ teaspoon, for greasing

2 just-ripe **pears**, peeled, cored and cut
  into bite size pieces

a squeeze of lemon juice

1 teaspoon ground cinnamon

100 g (3½ oz) caster sugar, plus
  1 teaspoon, to serve

225 g (8 oz) self-raising flour

1 large **egg**, beaten lightly

6–7 tablespoons **skimmed milk**

1 Preheat the oven to Gas Mark 4/180°C/fan oven160°C. Grease the sides of a 20 cm (8 inch) square cake tin with a little of the low fat spread and line the base with baking paper.

2 Put the pears in a bowl and toss them in the lemon juice to prevent them from discolouring. Add the cinnamon and 1 teaspoon of the sugar and mix until combined. Set to one side until ready to use.

3 Put the flour in a mixing bowl and rub in the spread with your fingertips until the mixture resembles breadcrumbs. Mix in the remaining sugar (reserving 1 teaspoon to serve), and the egg and milk to make a soft dough — you may not need all the milk. Put one half of the dough into the cake tin and gently press it out into an even layer.

4 Scatter the pears evenly over the top. Carefully spoon the rest of dough on top of the pears, spread it evenly and then press down gently to cover them completely. Bake for 40–50 minutes until risen and golden. Leave to cool for 5 minutes in the tin, then turn out on to a wire rack, place a plate over the cake and flip it over again, then sprinkle over the reserved sugar, and leave to cool. Cut into 12 squares.

 Cook's tip

This cake is made with the 'rubbing in' method, which produces a cake with a slightly dense texture. The pears should be just-ripe so they keep their shape during baking.

More to spend?

Delicious served warm with a 150 ml (5½ fl oz) portion of low fat custard per person for an extra 3 **ProPoints** values per serving.

Sour cherry scone cake

The secret to a successful scone is to avoid being too heavy-handed with the dough – be gentle and you'll be rewarded with a lovely light result. This scone 'cake' is best eaten warm, soon after making.

Serves 8
Preparation time 10 minutes
Cooking time 20 minutes
4 *ProPoints* values per serving
34 *ProPoints* values per recipe
Ⓥ ❄ (after baking)

225 g (8 oz) self-raising flour, plus
  1 teaspoon reserved for dusting
a pinch of salt
25 g (1 oz) caster sugar
40 g (1½ oz) low fat spread
40 g (1½ oz) dried sour cherries
100 ml (3½ fl oz) buttermilk
1 **egg**, beaten lightly

1 Preheat the oven to Gas Mark 7/220°C/fan oven 200°C. Lightly dust a non stick baking tray with the reserved flour.

2 Sift the flour into a mixing bowl with the salt and sugar. Mix together, then add the spread in small pieces. Rub in the spread with your fingertips until the mixture looks like fine breadcrumbs. Stir in the sour cherries.

3 Measure the buttermilk into a jug and beat in the egg. Pour the egg mixture into the bowl containing the dry ingredients, leaving a little to use as a glaze. Using a fork, mix together to make a dough. Bring the mixture together with your hands to form a round.

4 Put the dough on the baking sheet and gently press into a round about 2 cm (¾ inch) thick. Score into eight, cutting half way down into the dough. Brush the top of the scone with the remaining egg mixture. Bake for 15–20 minutes until risen and lightly golden. Cool on a wire rack. Serve slightly warm.

 *Try this*

This recipe also works with dried apricots instead of the sour cherries. Stir the same quantity of chopped dried apricots into the scone mixture for the same ***ProPoints*** values per serving.

Vanilla custards with sticky cinnamon plums

These traditional-style custards, flavoured with vanilla, star anise and cinnamon, are served with delicious syrupy baked plums.

Serves 4
Preparation time 15 minutes
Cooking time 40 minutes
3 ProPoints values per serving
11 ProPoints values per recipe

300 ml (10½ fl oz) semi skimmed milk
1 star anise
2 teaspoons ground cinnamon
2 **eggs**
25 g (1 oz) caster sugar
1 teaspoon vanilla extract
½ a kettleful of boiling water
12 ripe, firm **plums**, halved and stoned

1 Preheat the oven to Gas Mark 3/170°C/fan oven 150°C. To make the vanilla custards, put the milk, star anise and half the cinnamon in a small pan and heat just to boiling point. Remove from the heat and leave for 10 minutes to infuse the milk with the spices.

2 Meanwhile, whisk together the eggs and caster sugar until pale and creamy. When the milk has had time to infuse, reheat it to boiling point and then strain it through a sieve into the egg mixture and stir until combined. Discard the star anise and add the vanilla extract.

3 Pour the custard into 4 x 185 ml (6½ fl oz) pots or large ramekins. Put the custards in a baking dish and add enough boiled water to come two-thirds of the way up the sides of the pots. Carefully put the dish in the oven and bake for 40 minutes, or until set but still a little wobbly.

4 Meanwhile, put the plums in a small, non stick roasting dish, cut side down in a single layer. Drizzle 4 tablespoons of water over the top, then sprinkle with the remaining cinnamon. Bake for 30–35 minutes until the plums are soft and there is a syrupy sauce in the bottom of the dish.

5 Leave the custards to cool slightly, then serve with the plums.

 Try this

The baked plums are also delicious served with yogurt instead of the custard. Divide the plums between four bowls and top each serving with 60 g (2 oz) **low fat natural bio yogurt**, for 1 **ProPoints** value per person.

 Cook's tip

The custards and plums are served warm in this recipe but they are just as good cold. Both will keep in the fridge for up to 3 days.

Chocolate orange steamed pudding

This delicate pudding is infused with the flavour of orange zest. It's perfect served with 50 ml (2 fl oz) light custard per person for an extra 1 **ProPoints** value per serving.

Serves 4
Preparation time 25 minutes
Cooking time 1 hour
6 ProPoints values per serving
26 ProPoints values per recipe

40 g (1½ oz) low fat spread, plus
  ½ teaspoon for greasing
125 ml (4 fl oz) **skimmed milk**
40 g (1½ oz) plain chocolate, about
  70% cocoa solids, broken into pieces
40 g (1½ oz) caster sugar
2 **eggs**, separated
100 g (3½ oz) fresh white breadcrumbs
½ teaspoon baking powder
finely grated zest of a large orange
finely pared zest of an orange,
  to decorate (optional)
a kettleful of boiling water

1 Lightly grease a 700 ml (1¼ pint) heatproof pudding basin with a small amount of low fat spread.

2 Warm the milk in a small pan, then add the chocolate and stir until melted. Set to one side to cool.

3 If you want to make the decoration in Step 6, reserve 1 teaspoon of the sugar and then beat the low fat spread with the remaining sugar in a mixing bowl until pale and creamy. If not, use all the sugar now. Gradually beat in the egg yolks, followed by the chocolate milk. Stir in the breadcrumbs, baking powder and orange zest.

4 Whisk the egg whites in a clean, grease-free mixing bowl for about 2 minutes until they form stiff peaks. Fold them into the chocolate mixture using a metal spoon. Spoon the mixture into the pudding basin, cover the top with a piece of baking paper and then foil, and secure tightly with string.

5 Put a trivet or upturned plate in the bottom of a large lidded pan. Place the basin in the pan, resting on the plate or trivet, and carefully pour boiled water into the pan until it comes halfway up the sides of the basin. Cover the pan tightly and steam the pudding over gently simmering water for 1 hour until the pudding is just firm and risen. (The water should not boil away, but if it does, top it up with more boiling water.)

6 Carefully remove the basin from the water, remove the foil and baking paper and spoon the pudding into serving bowls. If making the decoration, shred the pared orange zest finely, then put into a small saucepan with the reserved teaspoon of sugar. Add 6 tablespoons of water and simmer for 2–3 minutes. Spoon over the pudding to serve.

More to spend?

A tablespoon of light single cream per person is delicious with this pudding for an extra 1 **ProPoints** value per serving.

Warm the milk, then add
the chocolate to melt.

Gradually beat in
the chocolatey milk.

Spoon the final mixture
into the pudding basin.

Olive bread swirls

There's nothing quite like freshly baked bread and these rolls make a take-to-work lunch into something special. Serve with Fattoush with Chorizo (page 42), Moroccan Squash Soup with Crispy Chick Peas (page 48), or Hot-Smoked Trout with Beetroot Relish (page 98).

Makes 8

Preparation time 20 minutes + resting
 + 40 minutes rising

Cooking time 15 minutes

3 *ProPoints* values per serving

21 *ProPoints* values per recipe

250 g (9 oz) crusty white bread mix
1 teaspoon plain flour, for dusting

For the olive and parsley filling

100 g (3½ oz) stoned black olives,
    drained
1 **garlic clove**, peeled and halved
a large handful of **fresh parsley**
1 teaspoon extra virgin olive oil
freshly ground black pepper

1 Make up the white bread mix according to the packet instructions.

2 While the dough is resting, use a hand blender or mini food processor to finely chop the olives, garlic, parsley and oil to make a thick paste — you may need to do this in two or three batches. Season with black pepper, to taste.

3 After the dough has rested, roll it out on a lightly floured surface until it is about 28 cm (11 inches) square and the thickness of a thin-crust pizza. Spoon the olive mixture in a thin even layer over the dough, leaving a 1 cm (½ inch) border around the edge. Roll up the dough, rather like a Swiss roll, enclosing the filling and pressing the edges to seal. Cut into eight thick, even-sized rounds with a sharp knife.

4 Place the rolls on a lightly floured non stick baking sheet on their sides, facing up, so you can see the filling, making sure there is enough space for the rolls to rise. Cover with cling film and set aside in a warm place for 40 minutes to rise.

5 Meanwhile, preheat the oven to Gas Mark 8/230°C/fan oven 210°C. Bake the rolls for 15 minutes until risen and golden. Transfer to a wire rack to cool.

 Freezing tip

You can freeze the cooked rolls in plastic freezer bags – they will keep for up to 1 month.

 Try this

For a non vegetarian version, instead of the olive mixture, try 60 g (2 oz) **lean ham**, torn into pieces and 40 g (1½ oz) half fat Cheddar cheese, grated, for the same ***ProPoints*** values per roll. Scatter these over the bread dough, following the recipe above from Step 3.

Roll up the dough, enclosing the filling.

Cut the dough into eight thick rounds.

Bake on their sides, facing up, like this.

Puffy pittas

These are great alongside a curry.

Makes 8
30 minutes in total + rising
4 *ProPoints* values per serving
38 *ProPoints* values per recipe

125 g (4½ oz) wholemeal flour
250 g (9 oz) strong bread flour, plus 1 teaspoon for dusting
1 teaspoon salt
7 g sachet fast action dried yeast
½ teaspoon clear honey
225 ml (8 fl oz) lukewarm water
calorie controlled cooking spray

1 Mix together all the dry ingredients in a large bowl. Add the honey to the lukewarm water to dissolve and gradually add the honey and water to the dry mix, first with a fork and then your fingers to make a soft dough. Knead the dough on a lightly floured work surface for 10 minutes until it is smooth and elastic. To test the dough, prod it with a finger and it should spring back when it's ready.
2 Clean the mixing bowl and spray with the cooking spray. Add the dough, cover with cling film, and leave to rise in a warm place for 1½ hours until it has almost doubled in size.
3 Preheat the oven to Gas Mark 6/200°C/fan oven 180°C. Heat two large non stick baking trays in the oven and spray with the cooking spray, or bake in two batches.
4 Divide the dough into eight pieces. Dust the rolling surface lightly with flour and roll out four of the pieces into rounds, about the thickness of a £1 coin. Carefully put the pitta breads on the hot trays and bake for 8–10 minutes until puffed up and golden in places. Remove from the oven and repeat with the remaining dough, if you have not cooked them all at once.

Simple soda bread

If you haven't made bread before, soda bread is the perfect place to start. It's quick to make as it doesn't need time to rise and is delicious served warm, soon after baking, or toasted.

Makes 1 loaf (20 slices)
Preparation time 10 minutes
Cooking time 35 minutes
2 *ProPoints* values per serving
40 *ProPoints* values per recipe

  (see Cook's tip)

375 g (13 oz) wholemeal flour, reserving
   2 tablespoons for dusting
1 teaspoon salt
1 teaspoon bicarbonate of soda
284 ml carton buttermilk

1 Preheat the oven to Gas Mark 6/200°C/fan oven 180°C. Lightly dust a non stick baking sheet with half the reserved flour.
2 Add the flour, salt and bicarbonate of soda to a large mixing bowl and make a well in the centre. Pour in the buttermilk, then gently mix with outstretched fingers to make a soft, slightly sticky dough.
3 Turn the dough out on a lightly floured work surface (reserving 1 teaspoon of the remaining reserved flour) and gently form into a smooth round loaf.
4 Place the loaf on the baking sheet and cut a deep cross into the top of the dough. Sift the remaining flour over the top and bake for 35 minutes until risen and golden. Transfer to a wire rack to cool.

 Cook's tip

Homemade soda bread keeps fresh for up to 4 days, but if you don't think you will get through the whole loaf within this time, you could halve the loaf and freeze it for up to 1 month.

ProPoints value index

On the go lunches

2 *ProPoints* values and under
Chicken tikka salad with sweet chilli
 dressing 36

4 *ProPoints* values and under
Monday lunch soup 16

5 *ProPoints* values and under
Fattoush with chorizo 42
Houmous, coriander and carrot
 wrap 24
Pâté, cucumber and mustard bagel 20

6 *ProPoints* values and under
Asian beef and lettuce wrap 38
Beef salad naan pocket 20
Chicken and pesto pasta salad 36
Creamy sweetcorn soup 18
Japanese chicken noodle salad 40
Mini ham quiches 28
Smoked trout salad 32
Tricolore wrap 24

7 *ProPoints* values and under
Coronation egg sandwich 22
Prawn cocktail pitta 30
Tuna and white bean crostini 30
Tuna pasta 34

8 *ProPoints* values and under
Cajun turkey bagel 19
Egg and 'bacon' roll 22

9 *ProPoints* values and under
Pastrami and coleslaw on rye 26

Meat free nights

1 *ProPoints* value and under
Moroccan squash soup with crispy
 chick peas 48

3 *ProPoints* values and under
Pesto soufflé omelette 74

5 *ProPoints* values and under
Cherry tomato tarte tatin 54
Hoisin tofu 74
Summer minestrone with aioli 46

6 *ProPoints* values and under
Filo egg baskets with fresh tomato
 pickle 76
Oven baked tomato risotto with Parmesan
 crisps 60
Posh beans on toast 68

7 *ProPoints* values and under
Italian Quorn and mozzarella bake 78
Mexican chilli beans with tortillas 70
Noodles with Sichuan peanut sauce 72
Roasted vegetable pizza 66
Sausage and aubergine hot pot with
 polenta 80
Warm halloumi, pepper and lentil
 salad 50
Winter chestnut stew with sweet
 potato mash 82

8 *ProPoints* values and under
Fusilli with creamy mushroom
 ragout 56
Leek, pea and mint risotto 62
Mushroom Wellington 64
Pear, polenta and soft cheese salad 52
Spring vegetable pasta with crispy
 crumbs 58

Short cut suppers

3 *ProPoints* values and under
Hot-smoked trout with beetroot relish 98
Mexican bean and tomato soup 86

4 *ProPoints* values and under
Lamb fillet with pineapple salsa 112
Minute steaks with quick tomato
 sauce 114
Spanish chorizo one-pot 93

5 *ProPoints* values and under
Flash-fried sweet chilli and
 garlic prawns 96
Stuffed portobello mushrooms 90

6 *ProPoints* values and under
Veg mac 'n' cheese 88

7 *ProPoints* values and under
Chicken pitta pizzas 104
Hot beef salad 92
Sausages with white bean 'mash' and
 red onion relish 94
Weekday roast red pepper chicken with
 baby roasties 108

8 *ProPoints* values and under
Chicken stew with gnocchi
 dumplings 106
Tuna and egg fried rice 100

9 *ProPoints* values and under
Pork and plum stir-fry 100
Turkey and spinach pasta bake 102

10 *ProPoints* values and under
Quick beef tacos 116

11 *ProPoints* values and under
Mint and lemon lamb couscous 110
Lamb with tomato dahl 110

12 *ProPoints* values and under
Ratatouille with bruschetta 88

Take aways at home

2 *ProPoints* values and under

Chapatti 150
Fresh coconut chutney 150
Saag aloo 140

4 *ProPoints* values and under

Chicken jalfrezi 132
Goan prawn curry 124
Lamb shashlik 140

5 *ProPoints* values and under

Beef rogan josh 142
Creamy vegetable pasanda 148
Fragrant rice 148

6 *ProPoints* values and under

Coriander fish with crispy ginger 122
Lemon and ginger chicken 136

7 *ProPoints* values and under

Chicken dhansak 130
Minced beef bhuna 144
Pork vindaloo 134
Spiced lentils with golden onions 146

8 *ProPoints* values and under

Balsamic chicken pizza 128
Sausage pizza 126
Special pork chow mein 138

10 *ProPoints* values and under

Oven baked fish 120

11 *ProPoints* values and under

Chicken laksa 136

Meals to relax with

4 *ProPoints* values and under

Yorkies with quick onion gravy 176

5 *ProPoints* values and under

Bubble and squeak cakes with
    eggs 158
Lemon, garlic and bay roast chicken 172
Welsh rarebit bites 160

6 *ProPoints* values and under

Great British breakfast 154

7 *ProPoints* values and under

Fish fingers with minty mushy peas 162
Pork and pear pot roast 174

8 *ProPoints* values and under

Sausages with mustard mash 177
Spiced cottage pie with parsnip
    mash 182
Steak with colcannon 186

9 *ProPoints* values and under

Cheat's chicken pies 170
Fish supper with homemade
    tartare 166
Honey mustard chicken stew with herby
    dumplings 168

10 *ProPoints* values and under

Beef, ale and mushroom pie 184
No-fuss fish pie 164
Prawn kedgeree 156

11 *ProPoints* values and under

Lamb steaks with roasted root
    vegetables 178

12 *ProPoints* values and under

Lancashire hot pot 180

Chill out desserts & bakes

1 *ProPoints* value and under

Tropical baked bananas 194

2 *ProPoints* values and under

Banana cinnamon muffins 200
Coconut drops 198
Deep apple pie 194
Marmalade and ginger
    cookies 206
Mixed spice, apple and oat
    biscuits 206
Simple soda bread 218
Strawberry posset 200

3 *ProPoints* values and under

Cheat's chocolate brownies 204
Lemon meringue semifreddo 190
Olive bread swirls 216
Peach crumbles 198
Strawberry and cream cupcakes 202
Vanilla custards with sticky cinnamon
    plums 213

4 *ProPoints* values and under

Cherry meringue pies 192
Dorset pear cake 210
Puffy pittas 218
Quick summer pudding 196
Sour cherry scone cake 212

5 *ProPoints* values and under

Honey, orange and almond cake 208
Marmalade bread and butter
    pudding 196

6 *ProPoints* values and under

Chocolate orange steamed
    pudding 214

General index